Contents — Continued

Illustrations

The California Condor, 1966-76:
A Look at its Past and Future

by

Sanford R. Wilbur

U.S. Fish and Wildlife Service
Patuxent Wildlife Research Center
Laurel, Maryland 20811

Abstract

The California condor (*Gymnogyps californianus*) was studied on about 900 field days between 1966 and 1976. In addition, some 1,000 items of literature, specimen records from 56 museums, and 3,500 reports of condor sitings by cooperators were analyzed. Distribution does not appear to have changed significantly since the 1930's, although there are some areas within the species' range that have become unusable. Two subpopulations of condors exist, one occupying the Coast Range Mountains, and the other found in the Transverse Ranges, Tehachapi Mountains, and Sierra Nevadas. There are well-defined seasonal movements within each subpopulation area. The surviving, wild population was estimated to be 45 condors in 1976, a decline of about 20% since 1965 and probably over 50% since 1940. No reliable population estimates are available before the 1940's, but it appears that a major decline occurred between 1880 and 1920. Shooting and specimen collecting were the primary causes of the early decline, and shooting continued as a major problem into the 1960's. Recent declines are a result of inadequate production; annual surveys indicate that only 16 young have been produced since 1968. Causes of low production are unknown but inadequate food supply, environmental contaminants, and disturbance from air traffic and petroleum extraction are implicated. A recovery plan for the condor is in operation; steps have been taken to supplement food supplies, preserve nesting and roosting habitat, and protect surviving birds from man-caused mortality or disturbance. The condor's prospects of recovery in its natural habitat seem bleak; a captive propagation program is proposed to supplement wild production.

◄
Frontispiece. California condors in Sespe Condor Sanctuary. (Photo by Fred Sibley)

Between 1939 and 1946, the National Audubon Society sponsored a study by Carl B. Koford of the breeding biology of the California condor (*Gymnogyps californianus*). His field work was concentrated on one condor nesting area in Ventura County, California. Library research into the history of the condor population, and occasional trips into other parts of the condor range, allowed him to publish a general overview of the species' history and status along with his observations of nesting behavior (Koford 1953).

Koford's work was followed in 1963-64 by a second National Audubon Society study, a short-term assessment of changes in the California condor population since 1946 (Miller et al. 1965). These researchers concluded that there had been a one-third decrease in the size of the population since Koford's study. Additional research into the causes of the decline seemed highly desirable, and following the establishment of the Patuxent Wildlife Research Center's Endangered Wildlife Research Program in 1965, a U.S. Fish and Wildlife Service researcher, Fred C. Sibley, was assigned to renew investigations of this species. He studied various aspects of life history and ecology, specifically concentrating on the effects of man-caused disturbances on nesting condors. After November 1969, I continued the research begun by Sibley, with special emphasis on condor food supplies and on factors inhibiting reproduction. This publication contains the result of our combined research.

Study Methods

Information presented in this report was derived from review of approximately 1,000 items of literature relating to the California condor and other aspects of avian biology, specimen records and field notes from 56 museums and private collections, about 3,500 condor observation reports from several hundred part-time cooperators, and the personal field work of Fred Sibley and myself.

Altogether, Sibley and I spent approximately 900 days in the field on condor research. Sixty percent of our time was spent in condor nesting areas, 17% in summer roosting areas, and 23% in condor feeding areas. During 1966-69, nesting studies absorbed 66% of field time, with the remaining effort divided between feeding and roosting area studies. In 1970-76, 56% of my field time was spent in nesting areas, 31% in feeding areas, and 13% in roosting habitat. Ten percent of total field time was spent on investigations in the Coast Range Mountains; most of the remaining time was spent in Ventura, Los Angeles, Kern, and Tulare counties.

Cooperators reported from all sections of the condor range, but coverage varied seasonally and geographically. Two-thirds of cooperator reports were for the period between June and October, when more people are in the field and back-country areas are generally more accessible. Also, condors are more conspicuous in summer and early fall because they are congregated in larger flocks in more accessible areas than at other seasons.

About 15% of cooperator reports are of condors in the Coast Ranges, 35% of birds in the Sierra Nevada and Tehachapi Mountains, and the remainder

Fig. 1. Locations of frequent observation points of California condor.

in Ventura and Los Angeles counties. Areas of frequent condor observations are shown in Fig. 1.

I have attempted to compare present-day condor numbers, production, and distribution with those of earlier time periods, but I recognize that this can be done only in a general way. Our research emphasis has been different than that of earlier studies; we have had a much larger group of cooperators reporting to us, and access into the condor range is now much quicker and easier than before. Also, reduction in total available habitat has changed condor distribution somewhat, and may have influenced flocking and migration patterns.

Species Characteristics

A detailed account of California condor behavior and life history is included in Koford's (1953) monograph on the species, so it is unnecessary to repeat this information. A general survey of the condor's basic characteristics, however, will help put later sections of this report in perspective.

The condor is a representative of the New World vultures, family Cathartidae, which are traditionally classified with eagles, hawks, falcons, and related birds (order Falconiformes). Some recent investigators (especially Ligon 1967) presented good morphological and behavioral evidence that New World vultures may actually be as closely related to the storks, family Ciconiidae, as they are to hawks and eagles (Fig. 2).

California condors weigh approximately 9 kg (20 pounds) and have an average wingspread of 3 m (9 feet). They do not attain adult plumage until 6 years of age. Because no immature-plumaged condors have ever been reported as part of a breeding pair, it is assumed that they do not reproduce until at least their 6th year. Condors in captivity have lived to be 35 to 45 years old, but the average longevity of wild condors is thought to be about 20 years.

Although not proven, condors likely stay with the same mate as long as both survive. The clutch is limited to one egg, laid between February and May in a cave or rock crevice; length of incubation is unknown. Koford (1953) reported one egg incubated a minimum of 42 days. In captivity, the egg of the Andean condor (*Vultur gryphus*) has required 54 to 61 days to hatch (Lint 1959; Olivares 1963; Dekker 1967).

The young bird is confined to the nest cave for about 20 weeks, and remains essentially flightless near the nest for another 10 weeks. Even after fledging, the immature condor is dependent on the parents for a number of months. Because the entire reproductive cycle may take longer than 12 months, most condors have been thought to nest biennially. Nevertheless, it now appears that condors may under some circumstances breed in consecutive years. Conversely, several species of long-lived birds are known to breed less regularly than is biologically possible (Broley 1947; Wynne-Edwards 1962), so the "normal" nesting interval for the California condor may be longer than every other year.

California Condor Habitat

Condors occupy a wishbone-shaped portion of California extending from Santa Clara County (rarely San Mateo County) south to Ventura County, then north to Fresno County (Fig. 3). This area corresponds roughly with the mountainous terrain surrounding the San Joaquin Valley: the Coast Ranges on the west, Transverse and Tehachapi Mountains at the south, and the Sierra Nevada on the east (Durrenberger 1965). Because the condor is a soaring bird, it depends to some extent on thermal updrafts and wind currents of mountain terrain for transport (Koford 1953:50). Historically, however, condors traveled far out over the almost flat Central Valley, as much as 65 km (40 miles) from foothill areas (Belding 1879; Stillman 1967). Recent re-

Fig. 2. Adult and immature condor in spread-wing posture, a behavior pattern shared with the storks. (Photo by Fred Sibley)

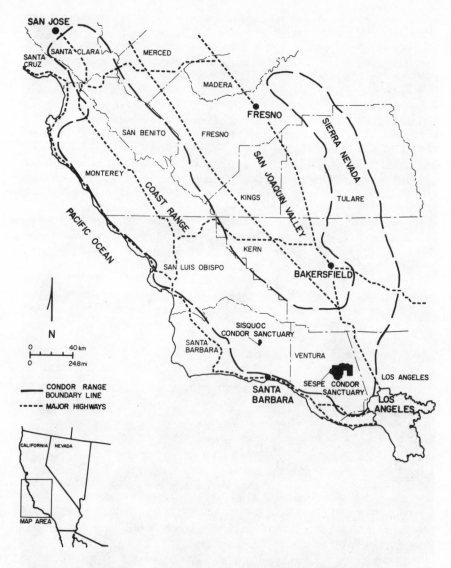

Fig. 3. Principal range of the California condor, 1966-1976.

striction to the more mountainous areas of the State is to a great extent a function of habitat availability. The San Joaquin Valley, formerly grassland with herds of native big game and domestic livestock, is now predominantly intensively managed cropland. The Los Angeles metropolitan area, with some 10 million inhabitants (Dooley et al. 1975), extends along the south boundary of the condor range for 150 km (90 miles) east and west, and 75 km (45 miles) north and south. Similarly, the San Francisco Bay area, with 4 million inhabitants and 7,400 km² (2,900 square miles) of urbanization and industrialization (Dooley et al. 1975), forms a barrier to the north.

Although downtown Los Angeles is less than 75 km (45 miles) from the principal condor nesting areas in Ventura County, the condor range itself is sparsely populated and, with only a few exceptions, receives limited human use. Thirty-six percent (1.7 ha) is in public ownership, principally administered by the U.S. Forest Service (Rieger 1973). Much of the 2.8 million ha (6.9 million acres) of privately owned lands is in large holdings. The largest single holding, The Tejon Ranch in the Tehachapi Mountains, includes 117,000 ha (290,000 acres), much of it open livestock range.

Climate.—The climate of the condor range is semi-arid, with 25 to 75 cm (10-30 inches) precipitation, falling mainly as rain between November and May. Snowfalls are usually light and of short duration. No rain falls over much of the area in summer and early fall. Annual temperatures vary from 0 to 43 C. One-half or more of the days during the year are essentially cloudless (Durrenberger 1965).

Geography.—Most condor habitat is located between 300 and 2,700 m (1,000-9,000 feet) elevation. This includes all of the Coast Range and Tehachapi Mountains, but only the western slopes of the Sierra Nevada. Distance from food sources may preclude regular use of higher elevations.

Condor nesting occurs in the area 610 to 1,372 m (2,000-4,500 feet) above sea level. The nesting areas are characterized by extremely steep, rugged terrain, with dense brush surrounding high sandstone cliffs. Principal plant species are several types of *Ceanothus*, live oaks (*Quercus* sp.), chamise (*Adenostoma fasiculatum*), silk tassel bush (*Garrya* sp.), and poison oak (*Rhus diversiloba*). Interspersed with the brush are small groves of bigcone Douglas-fir (*Pseudotsuga macrocarpa*), which are favored roosting areas for condors. The cliffs have numerous crevices and wind- and water-created caves in which condors lay their eggs.

Within the brushland (chaparral) community, there are small openings (potreros) dominated by annual grasses. In the Coast Ranges, through the Tehachapi Mountains, and in the foothills of the Sierra Nevada are vast areas of open grassland dominated by introduced annual grasses, particularly wild oats (*Avena fatua*) and cheatgrass (*Bromus tectorum*). Some stretches are almost treeless; others have scatterings of oaks (*Quercus* sp.), walnuts (*Juglans californica*), and related trees. In these open areas occupied by domestic livestock, condors find most of their food supply. Although all nesting sites are within the Los Padres National Forest, almost all condor feeding areas are privately owned.

In the higher portions of the Transverse Ranges, and above about 1,800 m (6,000 feet) in the Sierra Nevada, are stands of several species of conifers. These forest areas are occupied by nonbreeding condors as summer roosting sites, and the open rangelands below provide food for them.

Distribution

General Distribution, 1966-76

Within the range of the California condor, there are well-defined seasonal movements and use areas.

January.—Most condors are in the Sespe Creek-Piru Creek area of Ventura and western Los Angeles counties, and in the Tejon Ranch area of southern Kern County. Flocks in those areas sometimes include 10-15 condors, although the more usual group is about 4 birds.

Elsewhere, condors range widely through the Coast Ranges from the southern San Francisco Bay area south through Santa Barbara County; most sightings there are of individuals or pairs. Less regularly, individuals and small groups inhabit northern Kern and southern Tulare Counties.

February.—Most sightings occur in the vicinity of the Sespe Condor Sanctuary, and because the number of observations and flock sizes are similar to those in January, I think that the Tejon Ranch continues to harbor a large share of the population. Snow cover and poor road conditions preclude regular surveys in that area.

Distribution in the Coast Ranges is similar to January. Use of northern Kern and Tulare counties increases, and condors occasionally range even farther north in the Sierra Nevada foothills.

March.—Distribution in March is similar to February, although flock size in the Sespe area usually increases.

April.—Flock size in the Sespe area decreases as more condors move into Kern and Tulare counties. Kern and Tulare condors are apparently nonbreeding condors beginning a northerly movement away from the Sespe-Piru breeding region.

Coast Range distribution remains the same.

May.—The general trend in May is continued dispersal as singles, pairs, and small groups (three to five birds), although some flocks of six to eight condors are occasionally seen in the Sespe-Piru region in May. Sightings become more numerous in the Sierra Nevada foothills of Tulare County. Coast Range distribution remains unchanged.

June.—Populations in the Sespe-Piru region continue to decline, and most sightings and largest groupings are found in Tulare County. Flocks of 8-12 condors are seen, but it is more common to see 5 or less together. Coast Range distribution remains constant.

July.—The Sespe-Piru population is limited to a few scattered breeding pairs. Most condors inhabit Tulare and northern Kern Counties. In some years, perhaps because of food supply, a substantial population occupies the Mt. Pinos area on the Kern-Ventura County border. Flock size increases in July, and groups of 5-10 are seen.

August.—Condor use of the Coast Ranges and the Sespe-Piru area remains light, as most birds are in Kern and Tulare counties. Individual flock size reaches a peak in August and early September. Sightings of more than 10 condors together are common, and there are six records of 20 or more condors in a group during this study.

September.—In most years the majority of condors have moved south from Tulare County, although occasionally some large groups remain. Peak numbers are in northern Kern County in early September, then the birds begin a gradual movement southward into the Tejon Ranch area.

October.—Condors may be found in any part of their total range in October, but the majority are always found in the Tehachapi Mountains on and near the Tejon Ranch. Groups of 10-20 are regularly seen, and more than 50% of the total condor population is found in that area.

November-December.—Distribution is similar to that of October, with more use shifting back into the Sespe ·Piru region as winter progresses.

Sightings outside the range depicted in Fig. 3 may involve occasional vagrant birds wandering from their usual habitat. However, based on 15 records (most so far unconfirmed) from western San Bernardino and Riverside counties, I suspect that a few condors regularly use that region, at least during summer and fall.

Eight unconfirmed sightings in the Sierra Nevada foothills north of Fresno County suggest that some condors inhabit Madera and Mariposa counties, and perhaps even farther north, in some years. Although rumors of condors in the Sierra San Pedro Martir, Baja California, continue to be heard, it now appears unlikely that there is a resident population there (Kiff 1977).

Subpopulations of California Condor

The regularity with which condors are observed in certain areas at specific times of year, and in relatively predictable numbers, indicates that at least two subpopulations of condors exist (Fig. 4). The division in the population occurs near the Santa Barbara-Ventura County line. On the Coast Range (western) side of this line since 1966, I have only five records of four or more condors together; the highest count was only five condors (Appendix I). The highest possible composite counts (condors sighted at locations far enough apart to be different birds) during this period do not indicate more than 10-11 condors in the entire Coast Range area. As will be discussed later, nesting habitat in this region appears adequate for a considerably larger population, and food supply seems greater and more dependable than in the Sespe-Piru area. If there is free interchange between Coast Range and Sespe condors, it seems likely that greater use would be made of the Coast Range area.

Subpopulations are well known in other avian species. Common terns (*Sterna hirundo*) form individual cohesive groups that are self-sustaining and relatively free from association with other groups. Some colonies only a few miles apart are almost completely unrelated to one another (Austin 1951).

Herring gulls (*Larus argentatus*) segregate into subgroups for nesting and feeding (Drury and Nisbet 1972), and pink-footed geese (*Anser brachyrhynchus*) "form closed groups occupying small, well-defined areas" in which "the scale of mixing is negligible" (Boyd 1972). Although not always thoroughly studied, the high degree of "homing" to specific areas and nest sites shown by such diverse groups and species as waterfowl (Sowls 1955; Hochbaum 1955), common crows (*Corvus brachyrhynchos*; Emlen 1940), ravens (*Corvus corax*; Cushing 1941), eagles (Broley 1947; Brown 1972), and peregrine falcons (*Falco peregrinus*; Hickey 1942) not only suggests that subgroups within species are common, but also reveals how they are perpetuated.

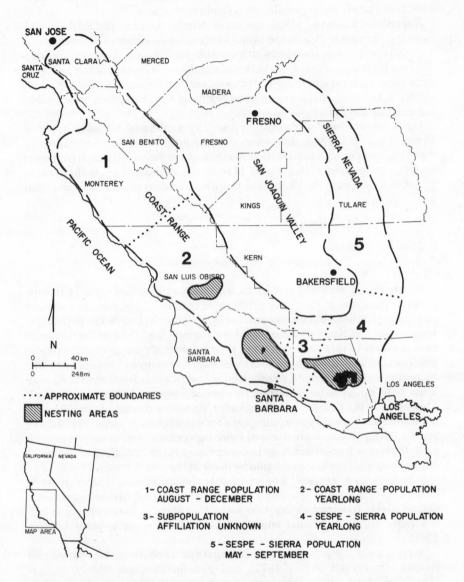

Fig. 4. Seasonal and geographical distribution of California condor subpopulations in relation to remaining nesting areas.

Changes in Distribution, 1966-76

No changes in either the overall range or areas used seasonally occurred during this 11-year period, but there were changes in the magnitude of use of certain areas. For example, condor numbers were high at Mt. Pinos each August from 1966 through 1969. In subsequent years, condor use has been "on schedule" seasonally, but total numbers have been much lower. August numbers in the Glennville area of Kern County were especially high in 1970-74, but some condors are usually in this area at that time every year. A few condors are usually in southern Tulare County in September; however, the 10-14 condors in that area during 1 week in September 1971 was an unusually large group for so late in the year.

Each of the changes noted appears related to differences in local food supply during particular years. Thus, individual condors are not so dependent on specific sites that they cannot respond to certain environmental changes. However, condors seldom seem to wander erratically, and they seldom appear at times or places where one would not expect to see them. Tradition, rather than food or any other factor, appears to be the major determinant of condor distribution.

Changes in Distribution, 1935-65

Condor range maps included in Koford (1953) and Miller et al. (1965) depict lesser distributional limits than I have described, although both reports include observations of condors north of their "normal" range in both Sierra Nevada and Coast Ranges. These birds were considered vagrants, but because neither study emphasized observations in the more outlying areas, it is likely that many visits by condors were unreported. Not enough data are available to make detailed comparisons, but it appears that there have been no significant changes in condor distribution spatially or seasonally since 1935, although there have been changes in magnitude of use in certain areas. Actual habitable acreage has been appreciably reduced as a result of increased urbanization and other changes in land use.

Although both Koford (1953) and Miller et al. (1965) apparently assumed one freely interchanging condor population, reports from their periods of study lend some support to my hypothesis that there are isolated subgroups of condors, and that this isolation is not a recent development. Condors passing between the Coast Ranges and the Sespe-Piru region would likely pass along the high ridges, past such locations as Nordhoff Peak, Reyes Peak, Whiteledge, Cuyama Peak, and Madulce Peak. Yet, even when large numbers of condors were known to be using both the Sisquoc Canyon area in the Coast Ranges and the Sespe-Piru area, and were believed to be traveling back and forth (Robinson 1940), observers at most of these locations reported condors only occasionally, and seldom more than two or three at a time (Koford 1953). At Madulce Peak in 1940, fire lookout B. Choice saw condors regularly, but they usually came from the Sisquoc Canyon area, circled near the fire tower, then returned in the direction from which they had come. Some condors could have circled up again high overhead and gone on to the east unnoticed, but if there was regular interchange in that vicinity, I think more evidence would be available.

Distribution, Before 1935

Koford (1953) discusses both the historic and prehistoric record of condor distribution in detail, citing Pleistocene and early Recent records of *Gymnogyps* vultures (either the current species or a very similar one) from California, Oregon, Nevada, New Mexico, Texas, Florida, and northern Mexico. He sets the post-1800 range as the Pacific Coast from the Columbia River between Oregon and Washington, south into northern Baja California.

Bones previously assigned to *Gymnogyps* at Shelter Cave, New Mexico (Howard and Miller 1933), have now been reassigned to *Breagyps* (Howard 1971). Locations where *Gymnogyps* skeletal material has been recovered are listed below.

1. Fossil beds
   Florida
   Reddick, Marion County (Brodkorb 1964).
   Seminole Field, Pinellas County (Wetmore 1931b).
   Hog Creek, Sarasota County (Wetmore 1931b).
   Itchtucknee River, Columbia County (McCoy 1963).
2. Tar pits
   California
   La Brea, Los Angeles County (L. Miller 1910; Howard and Miller 1939; Fisher 1944).
   Carpinteria, Santa Barbara County (L. Miller 1927).
   McKittrick, Kern County (Miller and DeMay 1942).
3. Cave deposits
   California
   Samwel Cave, Shasta County (L. Miller 1911).
   Potter Creek Cave, Shasta County (L. Miller 1911).
   Nevada
   Smith Creek Cave, White Pine County (Howard 1952).
   Gypsum Cave, Clark County (L. Miller 1931).
   Arizona
   Rampart Cave, Mohave County (L. Miller 1960).
   Stanton Cave, Coconino County (DeSaussure 1956; Parmalee 1969).
   Tooth Cave, Coconino County (DeSaussure 1956).
   Tse-an Kaetan Cave, Coconino County (DeSaussure 1956).
   New Mexico
   Rocky Arroyo Cave, Otero County (Wetmore 1931a, 1932).
   Howell's Ridge Cave, Grant County (Howard 1962).
   Conkling Cave, Dona Ana County (Howard and Miller 1933).
   Dark Canyon Cave, Eddy County (Howard 1971).
   Texas
   Friesenhahn Cave, Bexar County (Brodkorb 1964).
   Mule Ears Cave, Brewster County (Wetmore and Friedmann 1933).
   Mexico
   San Josecito Cave, Aramberri, Nuevo Leon (L. Miller 1943).

4. Indian mounds
   Oregon
     Brookings, Curry County (A. Miller 1942).
     Five Mile Rapids, Sherman County (L. Miller 1957).
   California
     Emeryville, Alameda County (Howard 1929).
     Santa Rosa Island, Santa Barbara County (Orr 1968).

Whether condors were year-long residents across the southern United States to Florida is not known. Part of the skeletal material from Howell's Ridge Cave (New Mexico), Rampart Cave (Arizona), and Mule Ears Cave (Texas) has been identified as belonging to nestling birds, indicating breeding at least east to Texas.

Koford (1953) did not include condor records north of the Columbia River, and tentatively concluded that all condors in the Pacific Northwest were vagrants from California, perhaps forced north in winter by food shortages. However, there are a number of apparently authentic records between the Columbia River and southern British Columbia (Douglas 1829; Macoun and Macoun 1909; Tolmie 1963). Also, although most records of condors on the lower Columbia River are from October to May, condors were present in the Pacific Northwest at other times of year. A specimen taken in the Columbia River area in 1825 was probably collected in late summer (Scouler 1905). Condors were observed in the Umpqua River area of Oregon from March through October (Finley 1908; Douglas 1914; Peale 1957), and in southern British Columbia in September and November (Macoun and Macoun 1909; Tolmie 1963). Information is biased by the small number of reports, and probably by seasonal travel patterns of observers, but it indicates year-long residency by condors in the Pacific Northwest. No condor nests were found in Oregon, Washington, or British Columbia, perhaps because few people visited the more rugged portions of this region before the species disappeared (Wilbur 1973).

Disappearance of condors from most of their range south and east of California apparently occurred with little influence by man. In those areas the condor was not a feature of Indian culture or legend as it was in California, and it was gone before man caused major environmental changes (unless primitive man was responsible for the disappearance of the large Pleistocene mammals, as suggested by Martin 1967). Increasing aridity in parts of the Southwest, and the loss of a significant vulture food supply following the disappearance of most large mammals (Mehringer 1967) may have been sufficient to make the area uninhabitable for condors.

In other areas, changes in distribution may be directly related to man's activities that caused entire subpopulations to disappear. For example, Monterey County, California, was once a major condor use area (Koford 1953), but the breeding population was apparently exterminated by shooting and egg collecting (to be discussed later). Although portions of the County still appear ideal for condor nesting, and condors are breeding a short distance to the southeast, nesting has not been reported since about 1902, and condors are seldom seen there now. A similar series of events occurred in the San Diego-Orange County area of California. If small, isolated subpopulations lived in the Pacific Northwest, Baja California, and elsewhere, the known impacts of habitat modification and direct mortality were sufficient to reduce those groups to low levels from which they could not recover.

Numbers

Population Size, 1966-76

It is difficult to estimate the total numbers of condors. Seasonal movements of the species involve some 4.5 million ha (10.8 million acres) of land (Rieger 1973), much of it rugged and isolated. Differentiating between individual birds and groups of birds is possible only on a very local and short-term basis (Wilbur 1975). Although more reliable observers than ever before are reporting condor sightings, there are still vast areas that are sparsely settled and receive only light and intermittent coverage. Considering these points, I think it is highly unlikely that all, or even most, condors could be seen in any given time period. Any population estimate based only on condors seen is probably low.

The highest positive count during 1966-76 was 34 condors on 24 October 1968 (Table 1). Several more condors can be safely added to this total. For instance, the October day totals include only two adult condors in Santa Barbara County, but an immature bird was known to be frequenting the area at that time. Similarly, only two of a known three-bird family group were observed in San Luis Obispo County. The third bird (immature) was known to be present both before and after 24 October, and was probably there on 24 October also. Four adult condors were still present in the Santa Barbara-San Luis Obispo area on 26 October, when two adults were seen far north of that region in Santa Clara County. It is unlikely that these birds came from outside the Coast Ranges, so they were probably not counted on 24 October.

Relating these 38 "sure" condors to the total population can only be done in a general way. During 1968 the current phase of condor research was well under way and key cooperators were reporting their sightings on a regular basis; therefore, probably few large groups of condors (more than five in a flock) could have gone unrecorded within the usual October range. In October, however, small numbers of condors are seen regularly in Tulare County, northern Kern County, and in the mountainous areas of western Ventura County; there are also confirmed and tentative sightings outside the "normal" range at this season. Considering the incomplete coverage of the possible range, it is highly likely that at least 10, and possibly as many as 20, condors were not reported. This would put the minimum population size in 1968 at approximately 50 birds and the maximum near 60.

Since 1968, both single and composite sightings have been fewer. Production during 1969-76 was about 13 young. Even if the long-term condor survival rate exceeded 95% annually, an extremely high level to maintain over a long period of time, mortality probably would have exceeded natality during that time. The current population almost certainly contains less than 50, and perhaps as few as 40 condors.

Changes in Condor Numbers, 1920-65

Koford (1953) estimated a population of 60 condors in 1920-50. Following essentially the same methods, but in a much shorter and less-detailed study, Miller et al. (1965) estimated 40 condors, a decline of about one-third between 1950 and 1965. The current estimate of 40 to 50 condors cannot be directly related to the results of those studies. Even trend comparisons are difficult because the observation staff is presently much larger than in earlier studies, local distribution within the overall condor range is somewhat different now, and some of the recent population information was derived from special "baiting surveys" that congregated birds near observers. After evaluating condor reports from various periods and estimating the effect that habitat changes may have on flock size and distribution, I conclude that the current population is smaller than in the early 1960's, and considerably smaller than in the 1940's and 1950's. If current condor population estimates are valid, both Koford (1953) and Miller et al. (1965) underestimated earlier condor populations.

If all condors belonged to one more-or-less freely interchanging, highly mobile population, it would be difficult to justify a population estimate much greater than the largest number of condors seen together at one time. For example, 20 condors seen in Tulare County 1 day could be the same 20 seen in Santa Barbara County 1 week later. Apparently both Koford (1953) and Miller et al. (1965) assumed complete and regular interchange, but as already discussed, this was probably not true.

If Koford's (1953) observations are considered on a subpopulations basis, his high single counts of more than 30 condors in the Coast Ranges and over 40 in the eastern segment of the range by themselves add up to a total population of more than 70 condors. Looking at the 1962 data (Miller et al. 1965), single counts of 8 condors in the Coast Ranges and 31 in eastern areas are recorded. Considering that some birds are scattered and unaccounted for at all seasons, a total well over 40 appears likely.

Comparing data included in Koford (1953) ʔnd Miller et al. (1965), it appears that the Sespe-Sierra subpopulation declined by about 10 birds between 1950 and 1965, and the Coast Range group by 15 or more. The number of dead condors found and the rumors of other losses in Kern County during the early 1960's (Miller et al. 1965) suggest an unusually significant period of condor mortality, and may account for most of the loss from the Sespe-Sierra population. Losses from the Coast Ranges appear to have been even more abrupt at about the same time, as 15-20 condors were roosting in San Benito County and foraging in adjacent areas until about 1963 (Miller et al. 1965; J. McIlroy, personal communication; F. Sibley, unpublished field notes). Movement of this number of condors in the Coast Ranges is well documented up to that time, and the abrupt cessation of reports suggests that some mortality factor affected the whole group at once.

Condor Numbers, Before 1920

Reliable condor population estimates are not available for the years before Koford's (1953) investigations, although figures ranging from 150 in the

Table 1. *Highest Positive Counts of Condors, 1966-76.*

Date	Number	Location	Observers
24 October 1968	27	Tejon Ranch, Kern County	R. Mallette, F. Sibley
	1	Snedden Ranch, Kern County	J. Borneman, G. Franklin
	2	Baldy, Ventura County	R. Fordice, T. Beck
	2	Salisbury Potrero, Santa Barbara County	W. Carrier, D. Connell
	2	Hi Mountain, San Luis Obispo County	R. Ferrari
Total	34		
8 August 1969	25	Mt. Pinos, Ventura County	J. Borneman, E. McMillan
	1	Cuyama Peak, Santa Barbara County	M. Jardequist
Total	26		
21 August 1970	22	Glennville, Kern County	E. Farnsworth
	5	Mt. Pinos, Ventura County	J. Leary, N. Snyder
Total	27		
7 October 1971	18	Tejon Ranch, Kern County	S. Wilbur
2 September 1972	24	Glennville	E. Farnsworth
	1	Cuyama Peak	G. Carpenter
Total	25		
25 October 1973	13	Tejon Ranch	J. Borneman, E. McMillan
	5	Tejon Ranch	W. Carrier, K. Axelson
	1	Hopper Canyon, Ventura County	M. Montagne, D. Warren
Total	19		

Date	Count	Location	Observers
17 October 1974	12	Tejon Ranch	E. Harrison, L. Kiff, R. Quigley
	2	Tejon Ranch	J. Tarble, G. Nixon
	3	Santiago Canyon, Kern County	R. Fordice, R. Buss
	2	Agua Blanca, Ventura County	R. Long, J. Blake
Total	19		
7 July 1975	9	Springville, Tulare County	J. Miller
	2	Gold Hill, Ventura County	M. Giorgis
Total	11		
14 October 1976	2	West Big Pine, Santa Barbara County	M. Montagne, D. Smith
	10	Tejon Ranch	L. Kiff, R. Quigley
	4	Tejon Ranch	W. and D. Clark
	3	Agua Blanca, Ventura County	M. Silbernagle, J. Lindell
Total	19		

1920's (Phillips 1926) to 10 in 1932 (Atkinson 1972) have appeared in print. The much more extensive range, and the frequent use in the literature of such descriptive terms as "particularly abundant" (Gambel 1846) and "common" (Newberry 1857) suggest a population much larger than today's, but even in the 1800's it was unusual to see flocks containing more than 20 to 25 condors. The only reports that I found of really large flocks of condors, 150 to 300 in feeding groups, are somewhat suspect because they are included in an article full of misinformation and hearsay (Taylor 1859).

Whatever the early numbers, the consensus is that the condor population decreased appreciably after about 1840. Cooper (1890) recorded that condors had "rapidly grown scarce" between 1840 and 1890, and Henshaw (1876) noted that the population seemed to be "very much diminished during the last few years."

Past Causes for Condor Decline

As noted previously, prehistoric decline in condor numbers was probably related to changes in the carrying capacity of large areas of habitat, as the great herds of large mammals became extinct and condor food diminished. Later, the almost complete conversion to urbanization and agriculture of such areas as the Sacramento, San Joaquin, and Salinas Valleys reduced condor feeding area appreciably, and numerous roads and trails were made into mountain nesting and roosting areas. Until recently, none of these changes caused a shortage of food or lack of habitat. Factors suggested as causing, or contributing to, the decline of condors are evaluated below.

Indian Ceremonial Use

The California condor figures prominently in the religion and ritual of several California Indian tribes. The "Panes" festival, which involved sacrificing a young condor each year, was widespread in the State, and many tribes collected and killed their own bird (Bancroft 1882). Another ritual, known as the "Aswut Maknash" or eagle-killing ceremony, was practiced by the Temecula Indians of Orange County. Condors presumably were sometimes substituted for eagles (Parker 1965). Kroeber (1925) mentions condors kept as pets by Indians in Kern County, and notes that condor feathers were used in various ceremonies among tribes throughout coastal California from Humboldt County to Mexico. Russian settlers visiting the northern California coast in the early 1800's found entire capes made of condor feathers. Some of these were taken to Russia and are still in existence (Vaughan 1971).

Condors apparently were still relatively common during the height of these practices, and there is no evidence such activity caused any significant population decline. Because the condor was highly revered, it is doubtful there was killing other than that prescribed by ritual. However, considering the low reproductive rate of the condor, it seems possible that tribal activity kept the condor population at least stabilized and possibly slightly depressed in some areas.

Killing for Feathers

Several writers refer to the great demand for condor quills to be used as gold dust containers. Dawson (1923) felt it was an important decimating factor, and suggested that hundreds of condors must have been killed for that reason alone. Another writer (Siddon 1967) claimed that "a 'quill of gold' became a standard measuring unit in the gold fields."

In Baja California in the 1880's, Anthony (1893) saw Indian and Mexican miners carrying gold dust in condor quills, and saw condors (three?) that had apparently been killed for their feathers. In Los Angeles County, California, in 1841 "New Mexican" miners were seen carrying their gold dust in "turkey buzzard or vulture" quills (the term "vulture" usually referred to the California condor during that period; Bidwell 1966). These two reports constitute the only firsthand information on the subject I could find. I read 16 journals written during the California gold rush, and although several record observations of the California condor, none mentions the use of condor quills for gold storage. Invariably, miners are described as carrying their gold dust in buckskin pouches (Leeper 1894; Borthwick 1917; Johnston 1948). If the practice of using quills had been widespread, it would seem that references to it would have survived from that era.

Douglas' (1914) reference to condor quills being used for pipe stems was quoted in several works, but he was apparently misinformed. The same source told him of condors laying black eggs, nesting in trees, and laying two eggs per clutch. California condors apparently have not suffered from the effects of millinery trade that the Andean condor reportedly did (Chapman 1917).

Capturing for Sport

In one of the earliest general articles on condors, Taylor (1859) tells of hearing about condors involved in "the same custom of capture and sport . . . practiced in Peru and Chile." Presumably men hid in pits and caught condors by the legs, then held contests with them against bears, dogs, and eagles. However, Taylor (1859) ". . . never had the opportunity of witnessing any of these fights." Harris (1941) made an extensive review of the literature of the period, and failed to authenticate such contests. My review of Gold Rush literature revealed numerous references to bear and bull fights, but none involving condors. If condor fights occurred, the total impact on the condor population was undoubtedly negligible.

There are reports of condors being run down on foot or horseback, or lassoed, but most apparently involved sick or injured birds (Koford 1953). The practice of "penning" — catching condors in an enclosure big enough for them to land in, but not offering enough runway to take off again — is also mentioned as a condor mortality factor, but mostly as hearsay or in reports questionable on other grounds. For example, Shields (1895) derived information on "penning" from a man who also told him about condors killing lambs. Several older popular articles mention condors killing their prey, but there is no firsthand evidence that this occurs.

Wanton Shooting

Mortality resulting from malicious or ignorant shooters is one of the factors most often cited as a major cause of condor decline. Cooper (1890) reported many being shot, and Dawson (1923) considered the cause of condor mortality "first and foremost, gunfire." In the 1940's, Koford (1953) thought it probable that one condor per year was being shot. The case against shooting is in part inferential, based on condor vulnerability and shooter opportunity and attitude (Miller et al. 1965), but losses to gunfire are better documented than most other mortality factors. I have records (Appendix II) of 41 condors shot more or less without reason between 1806 and 1976. Because condor shooting has been illegal for many years, it is probable that most shooting incidents are unreported or unobserved. Shooting probably has caused a significant and continuous drain on the condor population since the early 1800's, with the magnitude of this loss increasing following the advent of the high-powered rifle in the 1890's (Chambers 1936). One confirmed shooting loss has occurred since 1960. Credit for the decline in shooting losses goes to improved legal protection and greatly increased public education.

Scientific and Hobby Collecting

Collecting of condors and their eggs has been suggested by several authors as one of the chief causes of condor decline (Dawson 1923; Fry 1926; Scott 1936b). Koford (1953) estimated that about 200 condors and condor eggs had been taken as specimens, and concluded that "undoubtedly collecting activity has contributed significantly to the decline of the condor in some areas."

Analyzing museum and written records, I found evidence of 177 condors killed and 71 eggs taken for additions to collections. Also, 24 live birds were taken for exhibit or as pets (Appendix II). At least 111 birds and 49 eggs were taken between 1881 and 1910 alone, and in a single 2-year period (1897 and 1898) at least 20 condors and 7 eggs were secured.

The disappearance of condors from various parts of their range coincided with peaks of collecting activity in those same areas. Koford (1953) estimated that condors had become very rare in Oregon and Washington by 1840, in California from Monterey County north by 1890-1900, and in coastal Santa Barbara County and in San Diego County by 1910. He thought condors in eastern Santa Barbara County and Ventura County were holding their own through the mid-1940's. The main periods of collecting activity were: Oregon and Washington 1805-35, Monterey and San Diego areas 1880-1900, Santa Barbara coast 1891-1910, and Ventura County 1901-24.

If the condor population is viewed as a series of smaller subgroups associated with known or suspected subgroup areas, then a correlation can be drawn between condor disappearance and collecting activity. Because condors have such low replacement potential, isolated groups could be quickly reduced to a level from which they could not recover. Because of traditional ties to their own subpopulations, condors would re-pioneer historic range very slowly or not at all.

Canada geese (*Branta canadensis*) provide an example of how this loss of subpopulations and abandonment of suitable habitat might have occurred. Habitat from which the resident population has been removed (for instance, by overshooting) may never be repopulated, even though Canada geese pass by the area and "know" that suitable habitat exists there. Hochbaum (1955) believed this occurs because all geese with local breeding experience are gone, and traditional ties to other localities (even less suitable ones) are too strong for geese to break. Hesitancy in re-pioneering areas formerly occupied by their species is shown by various other species of waterfowl (Sowls 1955) and by the common crow (Emlen 1940).

In the Pacific Northwest, at least eight condors were collected between 1805 and 1835. At least three more are known to have been shot during this period. If there was a local population of 1, 2, or 3 dozen individuals (Koford 1953), known mortality would have been enough to jeopardize it. If, as seems likely, more were shot than are recorded in the literature, combined collecting and other shooting could have exterminated the bulk of the population and reduced it below a viable level. A remnant could have survived in the area until the early 1900's.

Subpopulations were apparently larger in California, but collecting effort was also much greater. Collecting in each subpopulation area continued until condors and their eggs were no longer readily obtainable. At the end of the collecting era in the 1920's, substantial numbers of condors existed only in eastern Santa Barbara County and in Ventura County, and collecting was intensive in the latter area.

Poisoning

Many ornithologists in the late 19th century reported major mortality of condors from feeding on strychnine-poisoned meat (Baird et al. 1874; Henshaw 1876; Ridgway 1880; Cooper 1890; Bendire 1892). Later researchers concluded there was little basis for these earlier claims (Dawson 1923; Robinson 1940; Harris 1941; Koford 1953). In analysis, all the early reports appear to be hearsay and all apparently originated from information supplied by Taylor (1859), but his paper lacks definite information, and merely states that condors are "often killed by feeding on animals . . . poisoned by strychnine"; it is not clear whether he ever observed this. Taylor included a number of highly questionable stories in his account (e.g., condors attacking and killing calves, lambs, and rabbits), and there is no clear-cut line between reliable information and fantasy.

I was able to find only three firsthand accounts of condors being affected by poisons. Fry (1926) in 1890 saw two condors that had died, apparently after feeding on a sheep carcass treated with an unspecified poison. In 1950 three condors were found near a strychnine-treated carcass; one died, two presumably recovered (Miller et al. 1965). Another condor was found in similar circumstances in 1966 and judged to be strychnine-poisoned. Following treatment at the Los Angeles Zoo, this bird was released back to the wild (Borneman 1966).

Although some condors have fallen victims to poisoning, there seems to be no basis for reports of "great numbers" dying (Henshaw 1876). It is doubtful that poison losses figured significantly in the major condor decline of the late 19th century, but occasional losses since then have probably combined with mortality from other causes to keep the population level depressed.

Because the condor population's delicate balance could be upset by virtually any change in either birth or death rate, everything that retards productivity or increases mortality must share responsibility for any reduction in condor numbers. However, the combination of wanton shooting and purposeful collecting occurred at the proper time and in the magnitude necessary to have caused a major reduction in population size. Had these two factors continued in full effect for another decade past 1925, even the remnant populations of Santa Barbara and Ventura Counties might have been reduced below viable levels.

Recent Causes of Condor Decline

Apparently no single factor has caused a significant loss of condors since about 1960. Of the 16 known losses, 3 were victims of accidents and 2 were shot. Causes of the other losses are unknown. Cumulative losses for all reasons have apparently been greater than productivity during the past 15 years, thus a reduction in mortality is mandatory if the condor's status is to be improved.

Production

Production, 1966-76

Estimates of condor production are based on actual observations of known nest sites, observation of condor activity in known and potential nest areas, and on numbers of immature-plumaged birds observed during population counts. From 1966 to 1969 most nest sites were visited individually and the contents checked; since 1969, observations of nesting areas have been substituted for actual nest checks. Estimates of production by year follow. The first number after the year is the estimated total production and the second is the number of successful nestings known for certain (i.e., active nest found or recently hatched young seen): 1966-3/1; 1967-4/3; 1968-2/1; 1969-2/1; 1970-2/1; 1971-2/2; 1972-2/2; 1973-1/0; 1974-1/1; 1975-2/2; and 1976-2/2.

In any year, nesting activity by individual pairs may go unnoticed, so estimates of total production may be conservative. However, it is unlikely that more than one nesting pair per season is missed. Condors are very traditional in their use of nesting areas, returning again and again to the same general localities and even to the same nesting caves. All sites (except one known to have been used only once since 1938) are in locations with a long history of condor use. The estimated numbers of successful nestings are therefore believed to be very close to the actual production.

The apparent decline in annual production shown in the above estimates is confirmed by sightings of immature birds in the population at large. In

October 1968, August 1969, and August 1970, composite records indicated possible counts of 10, 10, and 13 immature-plumaged condors in the total population, based on high individual counts and geographical distribution of individual immature sightings. The same criteria yielded "composite probable" counts of up to eight immatures in 1971 and 1972. In 1973 only six immatures could be accounted for; in 1974 only four; in 1975, five; and in 1976, six.

Decreased productivity is a result of less reproductive activity, rather than decreased nest success. In fact, the percentage of nest success may have been greater since about 1970. For example, of four certain nesting attempts in 1966, only one resulted in a fledged immature. In 1967, three out of six known attempts were successful. Since 1970 only one suspected nest attempt has been unsuccessful. However, nest checking has been less intensive recently, and some nests that failed early in the season may have gone unnoticed.

Comparisons with Production Before 1966

In 4 years of study (1939-41, 1946), Koford knew of 13 condor nesting attempts, 9 of which were successful (Sibley 1969). This average of 2.25 young per year is superficially similar to the 1966-76 average. However, Koford did not conduct an extensive nest search — in fact did not visit all known nesting areas — so he undoubtedly did not find all nesting birds. On 13 April 1946 he saw 12 immature condors simultaneously, all of which had to be younger than 5 years of age. The probability of having all immature birds together in one place at one time is extremely low, and Koford himself estimated that there were 15-20 immatures in the population. Therefore, four to five young per year is probably realistic for that period, which requires that the reproductively active number of pairs in the population, assuming biennial nesting and some unsuccessful pairs, numbered 12 or more. Thus, some 40% of the population was engaged in reproductive effort.

There is good reason to believe that Koford's estimate of 60 birds in 1940-50 was low, and his failure to recognize distinct subpopulations of condors probably resulted in an underestimate of the number of young birds in the total population. Actual figures for number and productivity should be increased but, from the data available, it appears that 40% is a probable figure for the reproductive segment of the population then.

Miller et al. (1965) did no nest searching during 1963-64, and their effort to collect and analyze reports of condors was less exhaustive than other studies. Their records of at least 10 immature plumaged birds show a minimum average productivity of 2.5 young, and indicate that at least seven or eight pairs were reproductively active (again assuming biennial nesting and some nest failure). Beyond that, no valid comparisons can be made.

Among the current population of approximately 45 condors, 85% are adult-plumaged birds. If reproductive activity began with attainment of adult plumage, if sex ratios were equal within the population, and if there was free mixing of all condors throughout their range, then a maximum of 19 pairs could be formed. Assuming that each pair nested biennially, 9 or 10 nesting attempts would be possible each year.

Actually, it seems likely that first breeding is deferred for some years after adult plumage is attained. A captive California condor was 12 years old before laying its first egg (Dixon 1924). First breeding in captive Andean condors usually occurs at 8 to 10 years (Lint 1959; Anon. 1976). Golden eagles (*Aquila chrysaetos*) attain adult plumage at about 3½ years, but do not breed until their 5th year (Jollie 1947; Spofford 1964).

The sex ratio is probably uneven in the condor population. My examination of museum records showed that 60% of the specimens taken were males. Sexes look identical, and most condors were collected away from nests, so there should not have been appreciable differential mortality from shooting. It has been hypothesized that males survive better than females in species that are not sexually dimorphic (Cody 1971).

Finally, the occurrence of distinct subpopulations limits the mixing of condors from different regions, reducing the likelihood that all potential breeding birds will find mates.

Minimum breeding age, sex ratio, and spatial distribution probably all affect the reproductive potential of the condor population. Unfortunately, we do not yet know the magnitude of each effect. If there are 60% males in both subpopulations, and if normal age of first breeding is 8 to 10 years, then there is the potential for 12 breeding pairs, or 6 breeding attempts per year.

Actually, only a couple of pairs attempt to breed each year, much lower than would be expected in any situation except an extremely disparate sex ratio. Determining the cause of reduced reproduction and correcting the situation is currently the key to condor survival.

Control of reproduction in birds and mammals still is not completely understood, but it is clear that success involves a precise blending of a number of factors. Photostimulation by increasing day length may be enough to induce a high level of sexual readiness in the male but not in the female. She requires interaction with the male before ovarian development is complete (Lehrman 1959; Immelmann 1971). Even when the internal physiology is wholly prepared, reproduction is greatly influenced by various stimuli and inhibitors. Stimuli such as adequate food or nest site availability act as releasing mechanisms that allow progression to the next stage of the reproductive cycle, and initiate actual nest building and egg laying (Lehrman 1959; Immelmann 1973). Inhibitors, such as sudden cold, fear, nest destruction, or chemicals, may block the reproductive process at any point (Marshall 1961; Cade et al. 1968). If inhibitors are too strong, or final external stimuli are lacking, reproduction will not occur (Marshall 1952, 1961; Immelmann 1971, 1973).

Food Supply

The relationship of food and welfare of the California condor has been discussed and studied for a number of years. Early researchers (Robinson 1940; Koford 1953) thought that food supply was already becoming a limiting factor in the 1930's and early 1940's. Koford (1953) described changes in food supply as the second most important factor affecting distribution and

Fig. 5. California condors and ravens gathered at mule deer carcass. (Photo by Sanford Wilbur)

numbers of condors in the past century. He thought direct persecution by man was the most important. A study made in the early 1960's (Miller et al. 1965), however, concluded that food supply for condors was adequate at all times of year, and had not been a limiting factor "since the 1920's." These later findings were based on what researchers considered adequate reproduction and an estimated overabundance of food within the condor foraging range. These authors apparently assumed condors were free to forage into all parts of their total range at all times of year, an assumption that is invalid. Miller et al. (1965) also failed to adequately differentiate between the total amount of food within the condors' range (i.e., all animals that die) and the amount of food actually available to condors (Brown and Watson 1964; Immelmann 1971).

Foods Eaten

California condors feed only on the carcasses of dead animals, primarily mammals (Fig. 5). Many species are eaten but, as Koford (1953) noted, domestic cattle constitute the most important food source by far. Cattle are even more important today than during Koford's research period, because domestic sheep have declined drastically in California (California Crop and Livestock Reporting Service 1970), and more are grazing outside normal condor range (Burcham 1957). Mule deer (*Odocoileus hemionus*), while possibly a "preferred" food (Koford 1953), tend to drift toward canyon bottoms to die (Blong 1954; Taber and Dasmann 1958), where steep terrain and brush interfere with condor foraging. Carcasses under brush are hard to see, and condors apparently cannot locate food by smell (Beebe 1909; Stager 1964). Thus, deer have probably never been a major food item for condors, and expansion of the deer population in some areas (Miller et al. 1965) and apparent declines in other areas have not altered condor food supplies overall. Ground squirrels (*Citellus beechyi*) killed by animal control programs have been locally important food sources in the past (Koford 1953), but are now seldom available in numbers. All things considered, an evaluation of condor food supply must consider cattle availability first, followed by other sources to the extent of their quantity, periodicity, and dependability within the condor range.

Amount of Food Required

A 9-kg (20-pound) California condor has a standard metabolism of about 350 kcal/day, as computed from the formula in King and Farner (1961). Converting to the metabolic rate of a free-flying bird is still speculative, because free-flying metabolism of other large birds has been experimentally estimated at from 2 to 4 times standard metabolism (Kahl 1964; Houston 1971; Jarvis et al. 1974). Depending on which is more correct, a California condor may have a free-flying metabolism of 650 to 1,300 kcal/day. Food eaten by condors has an energy value of about 1.25 kcal/g (Houston 1971), so the daily food requirement of the condor is from 525 g (1.1 pounds) to 1,040 g (2.2 pounds).

A captive California condor ate approximately 1 kg (2 pounds) of meat per day (Todd and Gale 1970), and maintained an average body weight of 9.98 kg (22 pounds; Todd 1974). Other large birds of prey eat daily amounts of food averaging 7 to 10% of their body weight (Craighead and Craighead 1956; Brown and Amadon 1968).

Condors cannot forage every day because of occasional periods of inclement weather, and I have seen them stay near roosting areas all day even in favorable weather. Probably the usual daily situation is that a condor either gets much more or much less than the average daily food requirement. African griffon vultures (*Gyps africanus* and *G. ruppellii*) can hold up to one-fifth their body weight in their crop and can rapidly store fat after a large food intake. Maximum fat stores and expendable protein have been found sufficient to maintain them at least 15 days without feeding (Houston 1971). Captive turkey vultures (*Cathartes aura*) deprived of food up to 11 days maintained normal body temperature and remained healthy (Hatch 1970). The California condor can undoubtedly respond in similar fashion.

In addition to supplying their own energy needs, successfully nesting condors must provide food for one nestling. The daily food requirement of a growing raptor is equal to that of an adult (Brown and Amadon 1968), so a breeding pair of condors require about 3 kg (6 pounds) of food per day. Condors usually feed their young every day, although nestlings have been known to survive without food for up to 45 h (Koford 1953). How the chick's ability to go without food compares to the adult is unknown.

Required Location of Food

Condors are able to travel long distances in search of food. Their normal soaring speed is estimated at 50 km/h (30 miles per hour; Koford 1953), and in midsummer there may be as many as 6 h per day in which atmospheric conditions are suitable for soaring flight. (In winter there are seldom more than 4 soaring hours.) Theoretically, condors might travel 125-175 km (75-100 miles) on a summer day.

Actually, effective foraging time and range are much less than maximum. Foraging involves much circling and searching, as well as direct flight. When a carcass is located, condors often do not immediately descend to it. If a coyote (*Canis latrans*) or golden eagle is feeding on the carcass, they may prevent condors from feeding for some time. On one occasion, I observed nine California condors waiting at a deer carcass for 45 min while an eagle fed.

Tradition is also important in determining food availability. As described earlier, condors are predictable in their seasonal distribution. Although they adapt to minor changes in food location, it is unlikely that under most conditions they would move far outside their normal seasonal range to search for food. For raptorial birds generally, attachment to a given traditional area has little to do with the resources available to that area (Craighead and Craighead 1956). Therefore, although food is available in Tulare County in December, it will not be available to condors who are traditionally elsewhere at that time. Neither would I expect condors from Ventura County to forage in San Luis Obispo County at any time of year, because the historic record suggests the lack of a traditional tie between those areas. As will be discussed later, traditions can be broken, but only with great difficulty, and with possible serious effects on other aspects of species' survival.

Distances between known nesting and roosting areas and regularly used feeding areas are generally less than 50 km (30 miles; Koford 1953). Although some food may be obtained at greater distances, breeding condors probably obtain almost their entire annual livelihood within 50 km of the nest. Nonbreeding birds are undoubtedly more flexible, but probably also obtain most of their food within 50 km of whatever roost they are occupying.

Current Food Situation

Coast Range Condors

There have been land-use changes that have made certain areas (e.g., the major valleys and areas close to cities) unsuitable for condors in the Coast Ranges. However, reports from county farm advisors and my own observations show that there are still vast acreages of rangeland well stocked with livestock and deer (Fig. 6). Little decrease in the condor food supply is anticipated in the near future. The maximum of 10 condors now using this area should have little trouble finding adequate food, although they may have to move considerable distances at times.

Fig. 6. Typical Coast Range feeding habitat for California condors. (Photo by Sanford Wilbur)

Fig. 7. Hopper Canyon, Sespe Condor Sanctuary, an important condor nesting and roosting area. (Photo by Sanford Wilbur)

A food problem may exist for breeding condors in the Coast Ranges. Although known nesting sites in San Luis Obispo County appear well supplied with local food, the area can support only a few pairs of condors because of few nesting sites. In Santa Barbara County there is considerable nesting habitat that has been used in past years, but the local food situation had apparently deteriorated by 1940 (Koford 1953), and the downward trend has continued. Deer numbers may be increasing near nesting areas in response to improved habitat, including the results of fire and brush manipulation, but livestock numbers have decreased on both east and west sides of the area (L. V. Maxwell, farm advisor, personal communication). I doubt that this area has enough food to support more than a few pairs of breeding condors.

Nesting areas exist in Monterey County that still appear suitable for condors and might be repopulated in the future. The food supply in that region seems adequate for several breeding pairs.

Summer is the critical food season in the Coast Ranges. Almost all livestock mortality occurs in late fall, winter, and spring. Occasional deer die-offs may provide abundant food in local areas at other times of year, but such occurrences are unpredictable and cannot be considered a regular part of the condors' food supply. The summer food slump in the Coast Range is sufficiently extreme that it may be a limiting factor in the expansion of the condor population.

Sespe-Sierra Breeding Population

The region in and around the present-day Sespe Condor Sanctuary, designated the Sespe-Piru area, has been an important condor nesting and wintering area since at least 1880 (Koford 1953), and probably for many centuries before that (Fig. 7). It is a logical choice because it is rugged and isolated, and has numerous sandstone cliffs with caves for nesting, coniferous trees for roosting, and shallow pools for drinking and bathing. Although there are other suitable nesting areas in other parts of the condors' range, the Sespe-Piru region is certainly the most expansive in terms of acreage and number of individual nest sites. Historically, it was a logical choice for a breeding area because of a food supply that was nearby and abundant throughout the year. Pronghorn antelope (*Antilocapra americana*), tule elk (*Cervus nannodes*), and mule deer were common within foraging distance (Dasmann 1958), and the local seacoast undoubtedly provided food in the form of dead whales, sea lions, and other marine life (Koford 1953). As native mammals became less abundant, domestic cattle and sheep increased and provided an alternate, and possibly more plentiful and reliable, food source. Potential food supply was well distributed in Ventura and Los Angeles Counties south of the Sespe-Piru area, and to the east in Kern County, making the nesting area the hub of a large foraging area.

Koford (1953) described various changes in livestock numbers and land use in the Sespe-Piru region that together caused considerable decrease in foraging land and potential food supply before 1940. For example, he documents a major decline in sheep numbers in Ventura and Kern Counties in the early 1900's and again in the 1930's. Although cattle numbers increased during that time, Koford (1953) concluded that the increase was not sufficient to make up for the loss of sheep as a source of condor food.

Since 1940 the local food situation has continued to deteriorate. Between 1960 and 1970, large acreages of condor foraging habitat in southern Ventura and northern Los Angeles Counties disappeared beneath new residential and industrial developments. The Agoura-Calabasas area tripled its human population in that 11-year period; the Thousand Oaks-Westlake district was 4 times larger in 1970 than in 1960; and the Simi Valley population increased 600% in that period (Security Pacific National Bank 1970). As a rough measure of loss of condor foraging habitat, I compared extent of urbanization shown on two sets of U.S. Geological Survey maps (7.5 minute quadrangles for Newbury Park, Thousand Oaks, Moorpark, Simi, and Santa Susana), the first completed in 1950 and 1951 and the second copies of the same maps photorevised in 1967 and 1969. In that 80,000-ha (200,000-acre) area, roughly 8,000 ha (20,000 acres) of condor feeding habitat have been completely urbanized in that time period. The actual loss is much higher because even where "rangeland" still exists, it has been divided into small parcels with considerable human activity and is seldom used by condors.

Outside the Simi-Thousand Oaks area, less drastic but similar events have occurred. Much of the remaining rangeland is held by land companies who plan future development. In a report prepared by the Ventura County Planning Department (1970), it was estimated that if current county and city policies are continued, in the next 50 years the current 92,000 ha (227,000 acres) of open "developable" land in Ventura County will shrink to 44,000 ha (109,000 acres). Little has happened in the ensuing 7 years to modify this prediction.

The general decline of sheep in California is reflected in Ventura County by a reduction in numbers of perhaps 25% between 1950 and 1969. In that same period, range cattle decreased from about 30,000 to 20,000 (E. L. Bramhall, farm advisor, personal communication). Much of this decrease was in the Moorpark-Thousand Oaks-Simi region, the foraging area closest to the main nesting areas of the Sespe-Piru region. In western Kern County, the number of cattle increased somewhat in recent years, but improved handling has reduced mortality so it is doubtful that the condor food situation has improved there (H. E. Thurber, personal communication). The future trend on the Tejon Ranch properties is expected to be toward fewer livestock, and more farming and other habitat-modifying uses.

According to various local ranchers and farm advisors, most livestock losses in this area occur between September and February, with only scattered mortality through the spring and summer months. Most deer mortality occurs during the same period (Blong 1954), although there may be major die-offs at any time of year. Overall, it appears that condor food may still be adequate in the area in fall and winter, but it seems highly unlikely there is now enough food in spring and summer to sustain a large number of condors.

Fig. 8. Feeding habitat used by Sespe-Sierra nonbreeding condors.

Sespe-Sierra Nonbreeding Condors

The foraging area of the Sespe-Sierra nonbreeding group of condors has been shrinking in recent years (Fig. 8). Citrus groves in Fresno and Tulare Counties have been extended several miles eastward into former rangeland. There has been a similar expansion of other farm crops in the area south and east of Bakersfield in Kern County. A trend toward dividing large ranch holdings into family "rancheros" of 8-16 ha (20-40 acres) is evident in Fresno County and southern Kern County. Although these small ranches remain as open space, they are of little value to condors because of related disturbances and a general lack of food, resulting from fewer livestock and more sanitary methods for the disposal of carcasses.

As in other portions of the condors' range, summer is the season of lowest food supply. There are less livestock on the range than in fall and winter, and there is no major livestock mortality during summer. From April through early August, it appears the condors must forage widely for food.

Possible Effects of Food Shortage

Although condor food appears in short supply, particularly in summer, there is no evidence that condors are starving, or are likely to do so in the near future. If, as seems reasonable, a condor requires 1 kg (2.2 pounds) of food per day, a population of 50 condors requires 18,000 kg (39,600 pounds) of food per year. Assuming condors obtain only 23 kg (50 pounds) of food from the average ungulate carcass (and many carcasses provide much more), only 720 carcasses will be required per year (60 per month). There are certainly many more than that available, although harder to find at some seasons and in some areas.

Besides causing actual starvation, inadequate food can cause birds not to breed at all, to defer breeding to an older age, to nest intermittently, or to nest unsuccessfully.

Failure to Breed

Immelmann (1971) stated that much circumstantial and some experimental evidence exists for the importance of nutrition in spermatogenesis and oogenesis in birds. Apparently, the reproductive function is a physiological luxury in time of food lack, and is then curtailed in favor of specific survival needs (Assenmacher 1973). Food, visually or physiologically, acts as a releaser for the breeding cycle. For example, wood storks (*Mycteria americana*) fail to breed if fish are not available at certain optimum levels (Kahl 1964). The reproductive cycle of long-tailed jaegers (*Stercorarius longicaudus*) may stop if food supply fails (Drury 1960), and some African birds of prey apparently fail to breed if they cannot find sufficient food at the start of the breeding season (Brown 1953). In some instances, if the normal food intake of the domestic chicken is reduced 25%, gonad activity almost ceases (Marshall 1961).

A limited food supply and the effects of social dominance may result in nonbreeding by some members of a bird population. Most populations have a hierarchy or "peck order" that ensures dominant members will fare better than those lower in the order (Davis 1952; Wynne-Edwards 1962). If food is scarce, only the most aggressive birds will eat, which has been shown in populations of griffon vultures (Houston 1971), and Marabou storks (*Leptoptilos crumeniferus*; Kahl 1966), and has been suggested for various seabirds (Ashmole 1971).

If an inordinate amount of time is required to find food, there may not be enough time, energy, or inclination left for reproductive activity. For example, royal penguins (*Eudyptes chrysolophus*) have only one nesting area and a limited nesting season. Although the ocean as a whole has adequate food, "there are obvious limits to foodfinding time and foraging distances beyond which breeding success is impossible" (Carrick 1972).

Finally, lack of food near nests may indirectly arrest breeding. Although traditional ties to breeding areas are very strong, continued lack of food sometimes forces populations to desert favored areas, permanently or temporarily (Lack 1937; Marshall 1951; Brown 1953). Adequate food may be the releasing stimulus of breeding activity, but the nest site may function similarly. If lack of food in one area forces birds to move into another area without adequate nest sites, reproduction might not take place (Lehrman 1959; Marshall 1961; Immelmann 1973).

It appears that food in the vicinity of the Sespe-Piru nesting areas may be inadequate to stimulate the reproductive function in some condors. Observations of condors feeding indicate there is a well-defined "peck order," with certain individuals and pairs dominating carcasses to the almost complete exclusion of others. General scarcity of food requires that condors spend long periods foraging, so there may be insufficient time for both foraging and reproduction.

I also suspect that food scarcity is the cause of an overall decrease in condor use of the Sespe-Piru nesting area during all seasons, and that this is inhibiting productivity. In the 1940's the area supported winter populations of over 30 condors, and 8-10 condors were seen regularly in mid-summer (Koford 1953). During the early 1960's, high winter counts included about 20 condors (Miller et al. 1965); summer observations of up to 4 birds together were common (U.S. Forest Service patrolman reports). Since 1965, highest winter counts have been of 11-13 condors, and summer records seldom include more than 2 birds together. Some of the decline in use is due to decrease in size of the total condor population, but the declines are not comparable in size or timing. It appears that most condors have shifted their winter quarters from the Sespe-Piru area to the mountains of southern Kern County, where a substantial food supply still exists in fall and winter. The traditional move into the nesting area at the start of the breeding season no longer occurs. There are few sites in Kern County that are comparable to known nesting habitat, even though feeding and roosting habitat is excellent much of the year. Stimulation to breed may occur only in the presence of typical condor nesting habitat.

Deferral of Breeding and Intermittent Breeding

Deferred breeding beyond normal minimum reproductive age has been shown to be a function of both nutrition and competition. As examples, in seabirds (Ashmole 1971), griffon vultures (Houston 1971), Canada geese and trumpeter swans (*Cygnus buccinator*; Palmer 1972), and pied flycatchers (*Ficedula hypoleuca*; von Haartman 1972), younger, inexperienced birds cannot successfully compete with established pairs for limited food supplies. In mammals such as the black bear (*Ursus americanus*) and *Odocoileus* deer, there is a direct relationship between minimum breeding age and nutrition; animals from food-shortage areas breed initially at an older age (Klein 1970; Jonkel and Cowan 1971; Robinette et al. 1973).

Breeding intervals greater than the normal biological limits may result if food is inadequate (e.g., Jonkel and Cowan [1971] relate nutritional levels to frequency of litters in the black bear). Condor food supply appears low enough that there may be deferred or irregular breeding, but minimum breeding ages and the reproductive performance of individual pairs are unknown. There is some evidence that the long period of juvenile dependency that often keeps condors from nesting every year (Koford 1953) is environmentally, rather than physiologically, controlled. That the species can lay eggs in successive years has been shown with captive condors, and is suggested by several instances when an egg was found in a nest from which one had been removed the previous year (Koford 1953). Dependence of the immature into the year following hatching is usually not due to its physical condition (it can fly to and from feeding areas with its parents by the end of the hatching year), but is the result of social pressure. Young birds cannot compete successfully at a carcass with either adults or older young, so adults must eat for their offspring as well as for themselves. Apparently variations in food supply do not change actual growth and development rates of young birds (Houston 1971; Ricklefs 1973), but if food is plentiful enough to allow young to feed unmolested at an earlier age, adults might begin a new reproductive cycle the year following successful nesting. That this may occur is suggested by the fledging of four condors from one nest cliff in four consecutive years, 1966-69 (F.C. Sibley, unpublished reports). This site is isolated from other nesting areas, and few condors use nearby feeding areas. Although there is no certainty that the same pair was involved each year, the site tenacity of individuals is generally well known among birds (Broley 1947; Austin 1949; Herbert and Herbert 1965; Coulson 1966; Brown 1972) and more than two adults are seldom seen anywhere near this particular nest site. The only obvious difference between this and other nest areas is an abundant nearby food supply and very little competition from other condors.

Unsuccessful Breeding Efforts

Inadequate food is known to reduce fertility in birds (King 1973) and mammals (Klein 1970; Robinette et al. 1973). Better conditioning promoted by good nutrition reduces mortality of young mammals (Klein 1970; Robinette et al. 1973) and probably of birds. Additionally, loss of eggs through chilling during long food-searching absences by the parents, or loss of nestlings to starvation, are possible food-related occurrences.

Currently, there is no evidence of food scarcity or any other factor reducing the success of nesting attempts. The few nests started in recent years usually have fledged young.

Food shortages may affect condors in less direct ways than those described above. As foraging habitat diminishes, condors are forced to congregate in fewer areas and in larger groups. This increases their vulnerability to shooting and other man-related mortality. Also, food shortage may cause mortality or reduced productivity under stress by mobilizing pesticides stored in the body. For instance, DDT may accumulate in body fat with no immediate toxic effects, and be gradually eliminated by normal bodily processes. However, if the system of the bird is stressed as during decreased food intake, stored fat is utilized and DDT is released in harmful — sometimes lethal — doses (Stickel 1969; Van Velzen et al. 1972). Pesticide relationships will be discussed later.

Disturbance

The reaction of condors to human activity varies with the duration and intensity of disturbance, whether it is noise or physical presence, and may involve flying, roosting, feeding, or nesting behavior.

Flying Condors

Flying condors show little fear of man and will often approach closely. They may even glide to a person walking along an exposed ridge, or sitting in an open area, and circle over him. Apparently the more conspicuous a person is and the more commotion he makes, the more likely a condor is to approach. Whistling and arm-waving may prolong the time the bird remains overhead (Sibley 1969).

Condors in flight do not avoid areas of human occupancy. I have seen them regularly over the oil fields near the Sespe Condor Sanctuary, and a regularly used condor flight lane follows Interstate Highway 5 through the Tehachapi Mountains. Condors are occasionally reported flying over Bakersfield, San Jose, and other cities and towns. Although there may be a limit to the amount of ground disturbance a flying condor will tolerate, most traditional flight lanes will probably be traveled as long as related nesting, roosting, and feeding areas are usable.

Roosting Birds

Condors usually return to traditional roosting areas each afternoon. At many of these roost sites, the same trees and rock ledges have been used for at least 35 years, while nearby perches that appear identical remain unoccupied.

Roosting condors are readily disturbed by either noise or movement, and disturbances late in the day may prevent roosting that night (Koford 1953). However, reaction to disturbance varies. On 31 May 1972, I walked to within 9 m (30 feet) of a year-old condor, took photographs, then entered a nearby bird blind. The young bird sat on the snag for another 30 min, departing then only because an adult condor forced it from its perch. In contrast, on 13 January 1970, movements of one person along a trail over 0.4 km (0.25 mile) from a roosting condor apparently caused it to change its perch several times and eventually leave the vicinity. Two condors roosting in a snag on 19 August 1971 showed no reaction to a sharp sonic boom, yet flew hastily from the tree when a fixed-wing aircraft passed within 300 m (1,000 feet) of them. A startling sonic boom on 7 October 1971 caused three adult condors to hurriedly leave their roost area.

Occasional major disturbances will not cause condors to abandon regularly used roosts, and they may adapt to general low-level disturbance. A summer roosting area in Tulare County is less than 1 km (0.6 mile) from radio towers, a fire lookout, and summer homes, yet is occupied by condors almost every night from May to September. However, noise levels are low and few people actually approach within 0.4 km (0.25 mile) of roost trees. Some levels of noise and activity will cause condors to permanently leave an area; two roosting areas were abandoned near the Sespe Condor Sanctuary. One area, on the west side of Hopper Ridge 1 km (0.6 mile) north of Hopper Mountain was regularly used by condors in 1939 and 1946. There was some disturbance in the area, including an occasional automobile being driven within 50-100 m (150-300 feet) of the site. Now there is a battery of oil wells

Fig. 9. Oil field development at the edge of the Sespe Condor Sanctuary. Condors formerly roosted along the ridge immediately behind the pumps. (Photo by Sanford Wilbur)

1 km (0.6 mile) away in line of sight of the roost trees, and there is almost constant, but usually low-level, noise and oil-related activity. Condors no longer roost on the west side of Hopper Ridge in that area, although they continue to roost within 2 km (1.2 miles) of the oil operation where roosts are shielded topographically from sight and most sound of the oil fields (Fig. 9).

A second roost site was located in cliffs of Pole Creek, about 2 km (1.2 miles) southwest of Hopper Mountain. Condors were seen there regularly in 1940 and 1941, and the regular presence of a very young condor one year suggests it may have been a nest site as well. There was a lightly-traveled farm road within 1.2 km (0.75 mile) of the roost, and some limited oil exploration had occurred about 1.5 km (1 mile) away. Now a major portion of the Sespe Oil Field occupies the area within 1.5 km (1 mile) of the roost, and there are producing oil wells within 1 km (0.6 mile). It has not been used by condors for many years.

No one was systematically documenting condor observations on Hopper Mountain during 1950-65, so it is not possible to show a positive cause-and-effect relationship between oil field development and abandonment of these roosts. However, lack of use at these sites, contrasted with continued condor occupation of traditional roosts just beyond the influence of the oil fields, suggests such a relationship.

Feeding Birds

Condors normally feed in relatively isolated areas and usually leave if approached within a few hundred meters (about 1,000 feet) by vehicles or people (Koford 1953). They seldom feed on animals killed on highways or in areas of regular disturbance. Koford (1953), however, recorded them feeding within 600 m (500 yards) of an occupied ranch house, and on several occasions I have observed them feeding within a few hundred meters (1,000 feet) of well-traveled roads.

Startling noises sometimes frighten condors from food; on 1 May 1969 a sonic boom caused four condors to fly up and the remaining two to run some distance from a carcass. On 2 May 1969 a sonic boom caused condors to fly from a carcass briefly, but a second boom elicited only a mild startle reaction (heads up, looking around; F. C. Sibley, unpublished field notes). One condor and six turkey vultures I observed at a carcass on 3 August 1972 showed no apparent reaction to a moderately loud sonic boom.

Condors have abandoned feeding sites once used regularly, but most such sites have a greatly diminished food supply as well as increased human disturbance. Probably the greater and more regular the disturbance, the less likely condors are to feed in the area.

Nesting Condors

Sibley (1969) plotted the location of condor nest sites in relation to roads, trails, and oil field activity. He found that, even though apparently suitable nest sites existed closer, no occupied nest sites were located nearer to various developments than the following:

1. *Lightly used dirt roads* — 1.3 km (0.8 mile) when the site was unshielded from sight and sound of the road, occasionally closer (0.8 km, 0.5 mile) when completely shielded.
2. *Regularly used dirt roads* — 2 km (1.2 miles) when unshielded, closest shielded about 1.2 km (0.7 mile).
3. *Paved road* — 3.5 km (2.2 miles).
4. *Oil wells* — 3.7 km (2.3 miles) when nest was in view of the well, 2 km (1.2 miles) when shielded from sight and most sound.

Both regularity and magnitude of disturbance are involved in discouraging condor nesting, as nests may be located nearer to lightly used roads than to regular travel routes or oil operations. Condors have nested very near intermittently used foot trails. It appears that the greater the disturbance, either in frequency or noise level, the less likely condors are to nest nearby. Since 1965 nests are known to have hatched successfully 0.8 km (0.5 mile) from an infrequently used administrative road, 1.3 km (0.8 mile) from a regularly used dirt road, 3.5 km (2.2 miles) from a paved highway, and 3.5 km (2.2 miles) from an operating oil well. Only 2 of the 10 nest sites used since 1966 are closer to any road than 1.6 km (1 mile). One of these, successful four times in a row, has not been used since 1969. Human disturbance at that site has increased appreciably in recent years, and may be the cause of current disuse, although there are other possibilities, such as death of one or both members of the resident pair.

Some nest sites used in past years now appear abandoned. Reasons for disuse are seldom obvious, but increased disturbance locally is a possible cause in some instances. As suggested for roost sites, I think that there is a maximum level of disturbance that condors will tolerate at a nest site. This undoubtedly varies with location, especially as related to topography, but it appears likely that condors usually will not nest within 2.4 km (1.5 miles) of regularly traveled roads or similar activity (Sibley 1969).

Even if nest sites are not permanently abandoned due to disturbance, noise and human activity may effectively thwart nesting success. Peregrine falcons subjected to repeated disturbance are thought to build up "some sort of cumulative nervousness" that may eventually lead to nest failure (Herbert and Herbert 1965). Bald eagles will stay near traditional nest sites in spite of considerable disturbance, but may not breed (Broley 1947). "Fear" reactions of various types are thought to inhibit breeding in birds, perhaps by curtailing ovulation (Marshall 1952, 1961).

It has been suggested (Moll 1969; Oehme 1969) that sonic booms may addle eggs and kill embryos, but laboratory tests indicate this is unlikely (Memphis State University 1971). Sudden loud noises have been known to frighten adult birds from the nest, however, causing them to break eggs or knock eggs or young from the nest (Ames and Mersereau 1964; Hagar 1969). Activity near nests has caused young raptors to fly prematurely, which sometimes resulted in their death or injury (Grier 1969; White 1969; Garber 1972).

Condors may not abandon nests despite repeated disturbance during the nesting cycle. Observations were made near one nest on 107 days during one nesting season, and the condors were disturbed at times by whistling, hand-clapping, and other human activity (Koford 1953). The young bird fledged successfully. Koford (1953) also reported instances where men actually entered the nest cave while nesting was taking place, with no apparent detrimental effects. However, broken eggs and dead chicks have been found at nests, and human disturbance has been implicated in some of these losses. For example, one nest visitor startled an incubating condor, which knocked its egg from the nest as it hurriedly departed (Sibley 1969). Two other examples that did not result in egg loss, but that show the potential, are also recorded by Sibley (1969). In the first, an incubating condor was startled by a man nearby, and in its haste to get up it kicked the egg several inches forward. On another occasion, a condor sleeping in a pothole virtually "exploded" from the cave when a sonic boom occurred, and it appeared visibly agitated for the next hour. Sibley (unpublished field notes) on two occasions was inside small nest-type caves when sonic booms occurred. He found the experience very unpleasant, and experienced considerable ringing in his ears.

Repeated disturbance of condors at nests might cause egg loss through chilling, or inadequate feeding of the young bird might result (Koford 1953). In addition, repeated disturbance during courtship might frustrate mating attempts. Sibley (1969) watched a courting pair of condors obviously disturbed by airplane traffic overhead. Each time a plane was heard, the displaying bird would fold its wings and look toward the sound, then begin again. If such interruptions were repeated regularly, courtship and subsequent reproduction might be inhibited.

Other Factors Possibly Affecting Productivity

Weather and Climate

Annual weather patterns and long-term climatic changes have been suggested as causes of reproductive variability, but the relationships are not well understood. High temperatures are known to stimulate egg laying in some instances (Davis 1955), but are thought to retard breeding in others (Sharma 1970). High humidity appears best for Indian white-backed vulture (*Gyps bengalensis*) reproduction (Sharma 1970). Humidity may also be important for the California condor, because Koford (1953) suggested that failure of three condor eggs was possibly due to the "dryness and coldness of the spring."

Within the current range of the condor, temperature and humidity vary considerably between individual nest sites every year. Certain years may be better or worse than others, but there is no obvious correlation between weather and nest success. The Northern Hemisphere has experienced a gradual warming trend since the late 1890's (Kalela 1949; Critchfield 1960; Nelson 1969), but the actual change in temperature has been small and variable from year to year (Critchfield 1960). It does not seem correlated with changes in condor reproduction since the early 1960's.

Minimum Population Density

Each population seems to have an optimum size at which it thrives best. If it falls below some minimum size, passing a certain "point of resistance" (Leopold 1933), it frequently becomes extinct (Allee et al. 1949). The mechanics of this minimum density have been described both genetically and socially. When a population has a small effective breeding number, certain genes become fixed and others lost. The population loses genetic variability, and certain nonadaptive or deleterious traits may become fixed in the population (Koford 1953). Socially, certain group activities seem necessary, in some instances, to stimulate and synchronize individual reproductive activity (Darling 1938). Also, a certain population level is necessary to insure prospective mates finding one another. For example, the population density of the rhinoceros on the Indian subcontinent is so low that it is unlikely that two rhinoceroses of opposite sex will meet and breed since they are very rare and the male's period of sexual activity is very short (Slobodkin 1961).

The genetic makeup of the California condor population is unknown, but applying the general rules of plant and animal breeding, it appears that the inbreeding coefficient may well be high enough to adversely affect reproduction (R. W. Allard, personal communication). Fortunately, species in which population size has never been large are frequently more resistant to inbreeding than other species, presumably because their genetic system evolved under some low level of inbreeding. That the whooping crane (*Grus americana*) population was able to increase even after numbers had fallen below 20 birds (McNulty 1966) is cause for hope that condor genetic makeup has not been irreparably affected. The cranes, however, continued to produce at a favorable rate even at the population's lowest point; the condors have not.

Although condor numbers, disparities in sex ratio, and isolation of subpopulations may combine to limit the number of pairs that can be formed, the effects of social stimulation are not so evident. Not all species require communal stimulation to release breeding behavior (MacRoberts and MacRoberts 1972), and the condor appears to be one that does not. Condors nesting successfully in San Luis Obispo and Santa Barbara counties have been completely isolated from other nesting condors, and seldom even join with others for feeding or roosting. In the Sespe Condor Sanctuary, I have observed pairs courting in company with other condors, but have never seen evidence that other pairs were stimulated by the display. Koford (1953) reports a similar lack of interaction between courting birds and others in the group.

Senescent Adults

If productivity ceases or declines with age, then a preponderance of old birds may not be breeding. Hickey (1942) suggested this as a cause of reproductive failure in peregrine falcons and California quail (*Lophortyx californicus*). It has also been hypothesized that, even if age does not bring sterility in peregrines, it may result in less success due to smaller clutch size, less intensive brooding, weakened attachment to the nest, and decreased capacity for finding food (Kleinstauber 1969).

The few definite available records of duration of breeding in raptors indicate senescence may not be a significant problem. Wild peregrines are known to have reproduced when at least 18 and 20 years of age, and a golden eagle in captivity laid eggs until it was 30 years old (Herbert and Herbert 1965). A captive California condor laid eggs until 32 years old (Koford 1953). However, if aging is a problem, it would be most likely in a species like the condor where individuals normally reach advanced age.

Insufficient Nest Sites

Koford (1953) lists the main physical requirements of a condor nest site as a cavity, usually in rock but in one instance in a tree, with: (1) suitable adult roosting perches nearby; (2) fairly easy approach from the air; (3) space below for taking off; (4) protection from storms, wind, and direct sun; (5)

space enough inside to hold two full-grown adults; (6) a level, sandy spot on which to lay the egg; and (7) perches nearby for the young bird after it leaves the nest. Adding these requirements to the need for relative isolation, and a strong preference for traditionally u; ed nest sites, it becomes apparent that there are only a few areas where condors are likely to nest. Despite these requirements, there seems to be no current shortage of nest sites within the limited habitat available.

California condors apparently do not defend a large nesting territory. Altercations between nesting birds and other condors are seldom seen, even though large numbers of nonbreeding birds have roosted close to active nests (Koford 1953), and active nest sites have been located within 1.6 km (1 mile) of one another. In 1946 and again in 1967, three active nests were known within a 7.75-km^2 (3-square-mile) area (F. C. Sibley, unpublished field notes). That particular area still appears physically suitable for that concentration of birds, and there are many other historically used sites within the current range of existing subpopulations that are not now occupied. If, as seems likely, the condor does not require more nesting territory than the 0.8 to 1.6 km (0.5 to 1 mile) estimated for other large raptors (Broley 1947; Vernon 1965; Grier 1969), there should be physical space for many more pairs to breed. Location of food near nest sites may, of course, be limiting.

Pesticides and Air Pollution

Poisoning has probably been a minor cause of California condor mortality but pesticides and other noxious substances are known to react in sublethal fashion in some species, reducing productivity and impairing individual vigor (Stickel 1975). Organochlorine compounds can cause death if weight loss resulting from reduced food intake, reproductive activity, or injury causes lethal mobilization of chemical residues stored in body fat (Van Velzen et al. 1972).

The effects of pesticidal contamination on California condors are unknown, but evidence is accumulating that there may be adverse relationships.

Body Residues

An immature condor that died after colliding with a power line in May 1965 had visceral fat concentrations of 18 ppm p,p'DDT and 30 ppm p,p'DDE (Hunt 1969). The bird had a full crop, was in good condition, and weighed a normal 8.74 kg (19.25 pounds; California Department of Fish and Game, unpublished report).

A second immature condor, found dead and considerably decayed in November 1974, had leg muscle concentrations of approximately 50 ppm p,p'DDE, plus much smaller amounts of other organochlorines (Patuxent Wildlife Research Center, unpublished report).

An adult female condor died in November 1976 after suffering a gunshot wound in the wing. At death it weighed only 6.04 kg (13.3 pounds). A sample of flesh contained 12 ppm p,p'DDE, and fatty tissue had 105 ppm p,p'DDE plus low amounts of several other organochlorines (Patuxent Wildlife Research Center, unpublished report).

Species differ markedly in their reaction to pesticides, so no firm conclusions can be drawn concerning the significance of these levels in the condor. In the first instance, the levels are relatively low, since residues in fat in a bird in good condition generally will be 10-20 times those in the total body. The levels in the adult bird were higher, but perhaps not unusual or unexpected for a bird that was in such poor nutritional condition. However, in comparison with other species, it seems possible that the concentrations found in the 1974 immature bird might have been enough to adversely affect reproduction in a mature bird or even cause death if fat mobilization occurred.

Eggshell Changes

The difference in pre-1944 mean condor eggshell thickness (0.79 ± 0.02 mm) and post-1963 thickness (0.54 ± 0.02 mm) is 31.1% (L. F. Kiff, D. B. Peakall, S. R. Wilbur, and R. L. Garrett, in preparation). This difference is both biologically and statistically highly significant. The thickest eggshell in the post-1963 sample was 23% thinner than the pre-1944 mean; the thinnest post-1963 specimens were 56.9% thinner than normal. Thinning of 20% or more is likely to result in reproductive failure and population decline (Stickel 1975). In nearly every study of eggshell thinning, DDE has been thought to be the major cause (Stickel 1975).

In addition to thinning, California condor eggshells collected since 1963 show abnormal internal structure. In photographs taken with a scanning electron microscope, a decreased porosity and an unusual compactness are evident (L. F. Kiff, D. B. Peakall, S. R. Wilbur, and R. L. Garrett, in preparation). This structural pathology is similar to that produced in eggs contaminated with chlorinated hydrocarbon pesticides (McFarland et al. 1971). Most of the post-1963 eggs on which measurements were made were found broken in the nest.

Although significant contamination is suggested by the above, a logical source of contamination has not been discovered. In general, concentrations of pesticides in condor food items are believed to be low. It may be that vultures metabolize pesticides differently than other groups of birds, resulting in greater concentrations. Turkey vulture eggshells have not thinned as much as condor eggs have, but they are 11-12% thinner than those collected before 1947 (S. R. Wilbur, in preparation). Andean condors collected in Peru had much higher concentrations of chlorinated hydrocarbons than other local species including the brown pelican (*Pelecanus occidentalis*), a species known to concentrate pesticides (D. W. Anderson, personal communication). In contrast, golden eagles, with a food source similar to condors, have shown no significant eggshell thinning (Hickey and Anderson 1968) or bodily concentration of pesticides (Reichel et al. 1969).

Effects of air pollution on birds have not been examined, but some detrimental effects have been found among mammals (Statewide Air Pollution Research Center 1973). The very rapid flow rate of air through the complex system in the body of the bird in flight suggests the possibility of undesirably high exposure. No monitoring of organochlorines or other air pollutants has been done in the vicinity of condor nests and roosts, but topographical and meteorological considerations suggest that air pollution levels may be high in these sites (P. C. White, personal communication).

Preservation

The California condor is immediately threatened with extinction, so threatened that the future of the species may well be decided within the next few years. If production fails to increase, and if annual mortality remains constant or increases over current levels, the species that has defied so many predictions of doom will at last disappear. The difference between the past and present is simply this: although the condor population has been declining gradually for many years, until recently numbers were high enough and production great enough that production deficits were low and the decrease was slow. This is no longer true. Currently production is low in a very small population whose average age increases yearly. Major losses due to old age could occur at any time, further reducing the population's potential for survival.

Although recommendations have been made for preservation of the condor (Koford 1953; Miller et al. 1965; Mallette 1970; Carrier 1971), and many have been implemented, the condor continues to decline. Past action was not wrong (had it not been for protection and management accomplished to date, the situation could be much worse), but it was not enough. While one problem was being treated, other factors continued to operate against the population. A comprehensive effort to attack all possible limiting factors simultaneously has been urgently needed.

The California Condor Recovery Plan

Steps to achieve this overall approach to condor preservation were taken with the preparation and implementation of a California condor "recovery plan" (California Condor Recovery Team 1974), the prime objective of which is stated as:

> To maintain a population of at least 50 California Condors, well distributed throughout their 1974 range, with an average natality of at least 4 young per year, and with the lowest possible mortality.

The basic tenets of the Plan are: (1) if condors are well distributed geographically so that all are not subject to the same local limiting factors and catastrophes; and (2) if annual production equals or slightly exceeds expected annual mortality rates, then a small population of California condors can continue to survive. The species would still be "endangered," but with continued intensive management, could become stabilized.

The Recovery Plan recognizes three principal needs of the condor population: adequate nesting sites, suitable roosts, and feeding habitat with adequate food. These must be available to each subpopulation of condors, and must be geographically and seasonally located to accommodate traditional condor use patterns.

Nesting Requirements

All nest sites known active within the past 20 years are on National Forest lands, and a plan for their protection has been prepared and implemented by the U.S. Forest Service (Carrier 1971). Two basic objectives are: (1) to restrict all motorized activity and blasting within 2.4 km (1.5 miles) of each condor nest site; and (2) to locate trails and trail camps out of direct line-of-sight of nest sites within a 0.8-km (0.5-mile) distance, and to continue restriction of the Sespe and Sisquoc Condor sanctuaries to all public use.

In general, the Forest Service has authority to manage National Forest lands for endangered species. However, administration of mining and mineral resources rests with the U.S. Department of the Interior. Restriction of such activities requires action by the Bureau of Land Management. Expanding oil development is now a major threat to nesting habitat.

Aircraft activity in the vicinity of nests may discourage condor use and may indirectly result in nest failure. A 914-m (3,000-foot) terrain clearance over nesting areas is now recommended on military and civilian flight maps, and the air space over the Sespe Condor Sanctuary is legally closed (Section 10501.5, California Fish and Game Code).

The value of all restrictions is increased by an active, well-rounded program of education, patrol, and law enforcement. Educational emphasis should center on the plight of the bird, and the justification for restricted use of nesting areas. Patrol will reduce the potential for violation of closures, and diligent law enforcement will act to deter further trespass in closed areas. As the condor requires the entire year to complete its reproductive cycle, restrictions should be in effect at all times.

Condors cannot breed without adequate nest sites, but production is apparently being limited by some other factor or factors. Inadequate food supply has been shown to result in reproductive inactivity in many species, and is believed to figure significantly in the decline of carrion-eating birds in South Africa (Houston 1971), Spain (de la Fuente 1964), and elsewhere. Supplemental feeding programs for vulturine birds have been initiated in Spain, France, Sardinia, and Austria (Bijleveld 1974). Our own experiences with an experimental feeding program for California condors show that condors will feed at bait stations without congregating in unnatural numbers or losing their "wildness" (Wilbur et al. 1974). Such feeding should be continued on a yearlong basis as long as there is any possibility that it is worthwhile.

There is enough evidence of chemical contamination of condors and their habitat to warrant a thorough evaluation of the effects of pesticides and air pollutants. The identification and removal of sources of contamination should be given high priority, as should laboratory studies of the effects of toxic chemicals on vulture reproduction and well-being.

Roosting and Feeding

Roosts are located on National Forests, and other Federal, State, and private lands. The U.S. Forest Service objective for protection of roosts is to eliminate all human activity within at least 0.8 km (0.5 mile) of the roosts (Carrier 1971). The same basic objective should be pursued for condor roosts on non-Forest Service properties.

Most feeding areas are on private lands. The basic need is to keep adequate food available in a relatively disturbance-free environment at those times of year that condors frequent any given area. A yearlong food supply is needed near nesting areas; elsewhere, requirements are seasonal. Preservation of food supply and feeding terrain near well-established nests and roosts should receive greatest emphasis. This may require outright purchase of key parcels, cooperative land-use agreements, and supplemental feeding. County zoning and land-use restrictions can often be made to favor the condor if they maintain open space and rangeland agriculture.

Protection from Mortality

Shooting, disruption of nesting activity, and possibly poisoning have the greatest potential for causing condor mortality. Mortality at nests will be limited by implementation of nest protection measures. Potential for shooting losses can be reduced by increased education, patrol, and law enforcement, and by firearms regulations and restrictions in certain condor congregation areas. The condor is legally protected by State and Federal law. The threat from toxicants can be reduced through cooperative planning of animal control programs, limiting extent, location, and timing to have least potential impact on condors.

Full and immediate implementation of the Recovery Plan seems to me to be a minimum requirement for perpetuation of the California condor. Without that, habitat for the condor will conti) ue to shrink in size and quality, further limiting survival potential. Although much effort has been directed toward preserving the condor during 1965-76, there are no signs of increased stability within the population. In fact, a significant decrease in production has occurred, and total numbers have declined during the last 10 years. I think that it is unlikely that the California condor can be perpetuated by only those relatively conventional procedures outlined in the Recovery Plan. Without interrupting action on the Recovery Plan, I recommend concurrent implementation of two additional measures: (1) establishment of new nesting areas, and (2) captive propagation.

New Nesting Areas

There are enough suitable nest sites for many more pairs of condors than have nested recently, but as mentioned earlier, condors have begun to congregate in an area well removed from traditional nesting habitat. One objective of supplemental feeding was to maintain and reinforce existing ties between breeding and nonbreeding areas. So far, this has not occurred. An alternative is to provide nest sites in the currently favored area in Kern County, an area that seems well adapted to yearlong condor occupation except that it lacks cliffs and caves for nesting. Structures made of artificial stone, such as are commonly used in captive animal displays, could be erected in isolated canyons in the Tehachapi Mountains away from most human access. Nest boxes have apparently not been used by vultures and might not be accepted by condors, but their provision would give the population one more option for survival.

Captive Propagation

At best, recovery of a totally free-living California condor population will be very slow. One method of accelerating population growth involves capturing several pairs of condors, holding them in captivity for breeding, and subsequently releasing their progeny to the wild. The condor's long period of sexual immaturity and inherently low reproductive rate are liabilities in such a program, but condors appear to do well in captivity and, barring accident or disease, can be expected to live many years. California condors have never been produced in captivity, but the Andean condor, in many respects much like the California species, has bred regularly in captivity (Janda 1939; Portielje 1949; Lint 1960; Olivares 1963; Poulsen 1963; Dekker 1967; Erickson 1974). Griffon vultures, similar in size and overall breeding characteristics to the California condor, have also bred and reared young in captivity (Bouillault 1970). In considering the opportunity to accelerate condor production, experiences with Andean condors at San Diego Zoo (San Diego, California) are especially noteworthy. In 10 years, one pair of Andean condors produced nine young, eight of which survived (Lint 1960). Rearing young away from the parents and hatching some eggs in incubators encouraged the adults to renest more often than they would have otherwise. A wild pair could have produced a maximum of only five young in the same time period.

Although capturing condors will reduce the size of the wild population, and might further reduce its breeding potential, apparently only a few pairs of condors are now responsible for the productivity of the entire population. Condor trapping could be timed and located to minimize the likelihood of capturing current breeders. Actual numbers in the wild would be reduced, but this would not necessarily reduce the reproductive potential of the population.

Objectors to captive propagation cite the lack of results in reestablishing captive reared birds in the wild. Admittedly much more research is needed but current projects involving peregrine falcons, bald eagles (Haliaeetus leucocephalus), whooping cranes, Aleutian Canada geese, (Branta canadensis leucoparela), and other endangered species have already produced results that are applicable to a California condor reestablishment program. Once Andean condor propagation techniques are perfected, release back to their native habitat is anticipated (Erickson 1974). All things considered, it seems likely that, by the time California condors are available for release to the wild, reestablishment procedures will have reached an advanced state.

Can the Condor Be Saved?

Because the California condor has survived so many predictions of imminent extinction, it would be comforting to assume that the species will go on forever no matter what. Complacency is nurtured by the almost certainly false belief of some that condors have been rarer and in worse circumstances in the past than they are now. The reasoning goes that if they have "saved themselves" before, they can do it again. Actually, consideration of the species' reproductive potential and the known losses since the turn of the century must lead to the conclusion that significant gains in population size were not only unlikely, but were nearly impossible.

McMillan (1968:42) stated that "there is considerable evidence that the entire species was close to extinction around 1908 . . . perhaps closer to extinction that at any time before or after." The discussion does not include an estimate of the population size, but McMillan and co-workers estimated that there were only 40 condors in 1965 (Miller et al. 1965). If the population was as endangered in 1908 as it was in 1965, then there were probably no more than 40 birds and possibly fewer. If there were only 40 birds in 1908, and if Koford's (1953) estimate of 60 birds in 1950 was accurate, then the population increased by 50% in 42 years. In addition to production needed to keep the population size stable, an average addition of one new bird every 2 years would have been required.

As discussed in the section on production, condors are probably not reproductively active until they are 8 or more years old. In a small population there are almost certainly uneven numbers of males and females. Because of the wide geographical range occupied by condors, probably not all condors have the opportunity to meet and mate. Finally, there may be adults in the population that have passed reproductive age. Considering all these factors, a population of 40 condors could include no more than five to six breeding pairs. Condors do not usually nest every year, so the highest annual production for so small a population would be two to three young.

Koford (1953) estimated 15-20 subadult condors (i.e., those in various subadult plumages) in his population of 60. Considering that other condors were incapable of forming pairs for the reasons outlined above, there could have been about 15 adult pairs. Assuming biennial nesting, seven to eight nestings per year would have been possible.

Starting with only two to three pairs laying eggs each year, population increase would have been slow initially. A possible progression would have been: 1908-21, three young per year produced; 1922-33, four young; 1934-40, five young; 1941-46, six young, and 1947-50, seven young. The maximum production at those rates would have been approximately 200 condors, but long-term "biological maximum" is never reached in a wild population. In the condor population, 50% success may be near the norm (F. C. Sibley, unpublished progress reports). Assuming a more optimistic 75% nest success, only 150 condors would have been produced between 1908 and 1950.

In that same 42-year period, a minimum of 17 condor eggs were taken from the wild, and a minimum of 55 condors died from various causes (Appendix II). Actual loss is unknown, but Koford (1953) assumed 5 to 10% annual mortality for the California condor under natural conditions. If losses to accidents, old age, and other "natural" factors averaged 5% annually, then 100 condors would have died in addition to the unusually high human-caused losses during that period. A mortality of over 150 condors is almost certain, so no increase could have occurred.

Much of the above is hypothetical, but based on what is known about condor history and population dynamics, the analysis is not unreasonable. Substituting other numbers and percentages will not change the conclusion that the California condor population does not have the capacity for significant increase now, and even more certainly did not have it during the early years of the 20th Century when mortality was abnormally high.

I agree with Koford (1953) that the California condor is most pleasing symbolically and esthetically as a free-flying, self-perpetuating species, but each passing year brings more questions about its ability to survive without intensive management. Since the passing of the wild big-game herds and their replacement with livestock in the mid-1800's, the condor has been dependent on the activities of man, and "naturalness" has been relative. Nevertheless, the wildness that is left in the species is desirable and should be preserved. If the species can be saved, we should also be able to preserve the aura and tradition of condor and condor habitat. It is not necessary to sacrifice "wildness" for "management."

The California condor is on the brink of extinction right now, and may disappear no matter what we do. If the species is to be saved, it must receive our most innovative attention as quickly as possible.

Acknowledgments

I have drawn freely on unpublished field notes and reports of F. C. Sibley. W. D. Carrier, U.S. Forest Service biologist, and J. C. Borneman, National Audubon Society naturalist, contributed many of the observations and concepts included here. R. C. Erickson, Assistant Director for Endangered Wildlife Research, Patuxent Wildlife Research Center, supervised the project and offered useful advice and direction. Members of the California Condor Advisory Committee and Condor Recovery Team also offered direction, particularly R. D. Mallette, California Department of Fish and Game, and R. C. Clement, National Audubon Society. L. J. Garrett, Patuxent librarian, provided published literature and helped to seek out obscure references.

Several hundred individuals reported condor sightings during the course of the study, among them ranchers, birders, hikers, biologists, and fire-control personnel. Employees of the U.S. Forest Service and California Department of Fish and Game provided the bulk of this information. Other reporters who furnished an especially significant quantity of information are: E. Farnsworth (Glennville, California), C. Osborn and M. Stieginga (both of the California Division of Forestry), W. Fieguth (Tejon Ranch Company), and the late D. Smith (Santa Barbara, California).

I am indebted to the following people who reviewed draft copies of this report, and offered suggestions for its improvement: J. C. Borneman, W. D. Carrier, R. C. Erickson, L. F. Kiff, C. B. Koford, R. D. Mallette, D. B. Marshall, H. M. Ohlendorf, F. C. Sibley, L. F. Stickel, and J. Verner.

References

Allee, W. C., A. E. Emerson, O. Park, T. Park, and K. P. Schmidt. 1949. Principles of animal ecology. W. B. Saunders Co., Philadelphia. 837 pp.

Ames, P. L., and G. S. Mersereau. 1964. Some factors in the decline of the osprey in Connecticut. Auk 81(2):173-185.

Anonymous. 1898. Notes on the taking of an egg of the California condor. Museum 4(7):103.

Anonymous. 1900. Two more eggs of California condor. Condor 2(3):60.

Anonymous. 1905. Annual report of the National Association of Audubon Societies for 1905. Bird-lore 7(6):295-350.

Anonymous. 1917. California condor on exhibition in Golden Gate Park, San Francisco, California Fish and Game 3(4):176.

Anonymous. 1976. Second stage of condor breeding program nears completion. Endangered Species Tech. Bull. 1(5):2, 4.

Anthony, A. W. 1893. Birds of San Pedro Martir, Lower California. Zoe 4(3):228-247.

Ashmole, N. P. 1971. Seabird ecology and the marine environment. Pages 223-286 in D. S. Farner and J. R. King, eds. Avian Biology, Vol. I. Academic Press, New York.

Assenmacher, I. 1973. (Discussion of nutrition in reproduction). Pages 68-73 in D. S. Farner, ed. Breeding biology of birds, proceedings of a symposium on breeding behavior and reproductive physiology in birds. National Academy of Science, Washington, D.C.

Atkinson, B. 1972. '40 dirty birds' hold their own but are never safe. Smithsonian 2(12):66-73.

Austin, O. L. 1949. Site tenacity, a behaviour trait of the common tern (Sterna hirundo Linn.). Bird-banding 20(1):1-39.

Austin, O. L. 1951. Group adherence in the common tern. Bird-banding 22(1):1-15.

Baird, S. R., T. M. Brewer, and R. Ridgway. 1874. A history of North American birds. Volume 3, land birds. Little, Brown and Co., Boston. 560 pp.

Bancroft, H. H. 1882. The native races. Volume 3, Myths and legends. A. L. Bancroft and Co., San Francisco, 796 pp.

Beebe, C. W. 1909. New World vultures. Part II. N.Y. Zool. Soc. Bull. 32:465-470.

Belding, L. 1879. A partial list of the birds of central California. Proc. U.S. Natl. Mus. 1:388-449.

Bendire, C. 1892. Life histories of North American birds. Smithson. Inst. Spec. Bull. 1. 446 pp.

Bidwell, J. 1966. Life in California before the Gold Discovery. Lewis Osborne, Palo Alto. 76 pp.

Bijleveld, M. 1974. Birds of prey in Europe. Macmillan Press Ltd., London. 263 pp.

Blong, B. 1954. A South Coast deer range. California Department of Fish and Game, Los Angeles. 27 pp.

Borneman, J. C. 1966. Return of a condor. Audubon Mag. 68(3):154-157.

Borthwick, J. D. 1917. The gold hunters. International Fiction Library, Cleveland. 361 pp.

Bouillault, J. 1970. Breeding the griffon vulture (Gyps fulvus) at La Fleche Zoo. Int. Zoo Yearb. 10:21-23.

Boyd, H. 1972. British studies of goose populations: hindsight as an aid to foresight. Pages 251-262 in Population ecology of migratory birds: a symposium. U.S. Bur. Sport Fish. Wildl., Wildl. Res. Rep. 2.

Brodkorb, P. 1964. Catalogue of fossil birds, Part 2 (Anseriformes through Galliformes). Bull. Fla. State Mus., Biol. Sci. 8(3):195-335.

Broley, C. L. 1947. Migration and nesting of Florida bald eagles. Wilson Bull. 59(1):3-20.

Brown, L., and D. Amadon. 1968. General life history summary. Pages 185-189 in Eagles, hawks and falcons of the world. Volume I. McGraw-Hill Book Co., New York.

Brown, L. H. 1953. On the biology of the large birds of prey of the Embu District, Kenya Colony. Ibis 94(4):577-620; 95(1):74-114.

Brown, L. H. 1972. Natural longevity of wild crowned eagles, *Stephanoaetus coronatus*. Ibis 114(2):263-265.

Brown, L. H., and A. Watson. 1964. The golden eagle in relation to its food supply. Ibis 106(1):78-100.

Burcham, L. T. 1957. California range land. Calif. Dep. Nat. Resour. 261 pp.

Cade, T. J., C. M. White, and J. R. Haugh. 1968. Peregrines and pesticides in Alaska. Condor 70(2):170-178.

California Condor Recovery Team. 1974. California condor recovery plan. U.S. Fish and Wildlife Service. 74 pp.

California Crop and Livestock Reporting Service. 1970. California livestock annual report summary for 1969. 36 pp.

Carrick, P. 1972. Population ecology of the Australian black-backed magpie, royal penguin, and silver gull. Pages 41-99 *in* Population ecology of migratory birds: a symposium. U.S. Bur. Sport Fish. Wildl., Wildl. Res. Rep. 2.

Carrier, W. D. 1971. Habitat management plan for the California condor. U.S. Forest Service. 51 pp.

Chambers, W. L. 1936. The hunter versus wildlife. Condor 38(5):199-202.

Chapman, F. M. 1917. Condor's quill. Bird-lore 19(1):5-8.

Cleveland, C. 1902. (San Diego Natural History Museum notes). West Am. Sci. 12(8):130-134.

Clyman, J. 1926. James Clyman, his diaries and reminiscences. Calif. Hist. Soc. Q. 6(2):136-137.

Cody, M. L. 1971. Ecological aspects of reproduction. Pages 461-512 *in* D. S. Farner and J. R. King, eds. Avian biology, Volume 1. Academic Press, New York.

Cooper, J. G. 1890. A doomed bird. Zoe 1(8):248-249.

Coulson, J. C. 1966. The influence of the pair-bond and age on the breeding biology of the kittiwake gull *Rissa tridactyla*. J. Anim. Ecol. 35(2):269-279.

Craighead, J. J., and F. C. Craighead, Jr. 1956. Hawks, owls and wildlife. The Stackpole Co., Harrisburg, Pa. 443 pp.

Critchfield, H. J. 1960. General climatology. Prentice-Hall, Inc., Englewood Cliffs, N.J. 465 pp.

Cushing, J. E., Jr. 1941. Winter behavior of ravens at Tomales Bay, California. Condor 43(2):103-107.

Darling, F. F. 1938. Bird flocks and the breeding cycle. A contribution to the study of avian sociality. Cambridge University Press, London and New York. 124 pp.

Dasmann, W. P. 1958. Big game of California. California Department of Fish and Game. 56 pp.

Davie, O. 1898. Nests and eggs of North American birds. David McKay, Philadelphia. 509 pp.

Davis, D. E. 1952. Social behavior and reproduction. Auk 69(2):171-182.

Davis, D. E. 1955. Breeding biology of birds. Pages 264-308 *in* A. Wolfson, ed. Recent studies in avian biology. University of Illinois Press, Urbana.

Dawson, W. L. 1923. The birds of California. South Moulton Co., San Diego. 2121 pp.

Dekker, D. 1967. Hand-rearing the Andean condor at Amsterdam Zoo. Int. Zoo Yearb. 7:227-228.

De la Ascension, A. 1928. Father Antonio de la Ascension's account of the voyage of Sebastian Vizcaino. Calif. Hist. Soc. Q. 7(4):295-394.

De la Fuente, F. R. 1964. Status of predatory birds in Spain. Pages 120-123 *in* International Council for Bird Preservation, Proceedings of the Working Conference on Birds of Prey and Owls. 10-12 April 1964. Caen, France.

DeSaussure, R. 1956. Remains of the California condor in Arizona caves. Plateau 29(2):44-45.

Dixon, J. 1924. California condors breed in captivity. Condor 26(5):192.

Dooley, E. J., R. W. Durrenberger, and A. F. Rolle. 1975. California. Pages 32-53 *in* The World Book Encyclopedia, Volume 3. Field Enterprises Educational Corp., Chicago.

Douglas, D. 1829. Observations on *Vultur Californianus* of Shaw. Vigor's Zool. J. 4(1):328-330.

Douglas, D. 1914. Journal kept by David Douglas during his travels in North America, 1823-1827. William Wesley and Son, London. 364 pp.

Drury, W. H. 1960. Breeding activities of long-tailed jaeger, herring gull and arctic tern on Bylot Island, Northwest Territories, Canada. Bird-banding 21(2):63-79.

Drury, W. H., and I. C. T. Nisbet. 1972. The importance of movements in the biology of herring gulls in New England. Pages 173-213 in Population ecology of migratory birds: a symposium. U.S. Bur. Sport Fish. Wildl., Wildl. Res. Rep. 2.

Durrenberger, R. W. 1965. Patterns on the land: geographical, historical and political maps of California. National Press Books, Palo Alto. 109 pp.

Emlen, J. T. 1940. The midwinter distribution of the crow in California. Condor 42(6):287-294.

Erickson, R. C. 1974. Andean condor studies at Patuxent and California condor contingency planning. Paper presented at California Condor Recovery Team meeting, 1 October 1974, Fresno, Calif. 5 pp.

Finley, W. L. 1908. Life history of the California condor. Part II. Condor 10(1):5-10.

Fisher, H. I. 1944. The skulls of the cathartid vultures. Condor 46(6):272-296.

Fry, W. 1926. The California condor — a modern roc. Gull 8(5):1-3.

Gambel, W. 1946. Remarks on the birds observed in upper California. Proc. Acad. Nat. Sci. Phila. 3:44-48.

Garber, D. P. 1972. Osprey study, Lassen and Plumas Counties, California, 1970-1971. Calif. Dep. Fish Game, Admin. Rep. 72-1. 33 pp.

Gass, P. 1904. Gass's journal of the Lewis and Clark expedition. Reprint of edition of 1811. A. C. McClurg and Co., Chicago. 298 pp.

Grier, J. W. 1969. Bald eagle behavior and productivity responses to climbing to nests. J. Wildl. Manage. 33(4):961-966.

Grinnell, J. 1909. Editorial notes and news. Condor 11(3):104.

Grinnell, J. 1928. A distributional summation of the ornithology of Lower California. Univ. California Publ. Zool. 32(1):1-300.

Hagar, J. A. 1969. History of the Massachusetts peregrine falcon population, 1935-57. Pages 123-131 in J. J. Hickey, ed. Peregrine falcon populations, their biology and decline. University of Wisconsin Press, Madison.

Harris, H. 1941. The annals of Gymnogyps to 1900. Condor 43(1):3-55.

Hatch, D. E. 1970. Energy conserving and heat dissipating mechanisms of the turkey vulture. Auk 87(1):111-124.

Herbert, R. A., and K. G. S. Herbert. 1965. Behavior of peregrine falcons in the New York City Region. Auk 82(1):62-94.

Henshaw, H. W. 1876. Report on the ornithology of the portions of California visited during the field season of 1875. Pages 224-278 in G. M. Wheeler. Annual report upon the geographical survey west of the 100th Meridian in California, Nevada, Utah, Colorado, Wyoming, New Mexico, Arizona and Montana. U.S. Government Printing Office, Washington, D.C.

Hickey, J. J. 1942. Eastern population of the duck hawk. Auk 59(2):176-204.

Hickey, J. J., and D. W. Anderson. 1968. Chlorinated hydrocarbons and eggshell changes in raptorial and fish-eating birds. Science 162(3850):271-273.

Hochbaum, H. A. 1955. Travels and traditions of waterfowl. Charles T. Branford Co., Newton, Mass. 301 pp.

Hoffman, W. H. 1895. Notes on California condors. Avifauna 1(2):17-19.

Holmes, F. H. 1897. A pet condor. Nidologist 4(6):58-59.

Houston, D. C. 1971. The ecology of Serengeti vultures. Ph.D. thesis. Trinity College, Oxford University, England. 193 pp.

Howard, H. 1929. The avifauna of Emeryville shellmound. Univ. Calif. Publ. Zool. 32(2):301-394.

Howard, H. 1938. (Cooper Ornithological Society meeting notes). Condor 40(3):132.

Howard, H. 1952. The prehistoric avifauna of Smith Creek Cave, Nevada, with a description of a new gigantic raptor. Bull. South. Calif. Acad. Sci. 51(2):50-54.

Howard, H. 1962. Bird remains from a prehistoric cave deposit in Grant County, New Mexico. Condor 64(3):241-242.

Howard, H. 1971. Quaternary avian remains from Dark Canyon Cave, New Mexico. Condor 73(2):237-240.

Howard, H., and A. H. Miller. 1933. Bird remains from cave deposits in New Mexico. Condor 35(1):15-18.

Howard, H., and A. H. Miller. 1939. The avifauna associated with human remains at Rancho La Brea, California. Carnegie Inst. Publ. 514:39-48.

Hunt, E. G. 1969. Pesticide residues in fish and wildlife of California. Pages 455-460 *in* J. J. Hickey, ed. Peregrine falcon populations, their biology and decline. University of Wisconsin Press, Madison.

Immelmann, K. 1971. Ecological aspects of periodic reproduction. Pages 341-389 *in* D. S. Farner and J. R. King, eds. Avian biology, Volume I. Academic Press, New York.

Immelmann, K. 1973. Role of the environment in reproduction as source of "predictive" information. Pages 121-147 *in* D. S. Farner, ed. Breeding biology of birds. National Academy of Science, Washington, D.C.

Janda, J. 1939. Eine gelungene Kondorbrut (A successful breeding of condors). Der Zool. Garten N. F., 10:94-96.

Jarvis, M. J. F., W. R. Siegfried, and M. H. Currie. 1974. Conservation of the Cape vulture in the Cape Province. J. S. Afr. Wildl. Manage. Assoc. 4(1):29-34.

Johnston, W. G. 1948. Overland to California. Biobooks, Oakland, California. 272 pp.

Jollie, M. 1947. Plumage changes in the golden eagle. Auk 64(4):549-576.

Jonkel, C. J., and I. McT. Cowan. 1971. The black bear in the spruce-fir forest. Wildl. Monogr. 27:1-57.

Kahl, M. P. 1964. Food ecology of the wood stork (*Mycteria americana*) in Florida. Ecol. Monogr. 34:97-117.

Kahl, M. P. 1966. A contribution to the ecology and reproductive biology of the marabou stork (*Leptotilos cruminiferus*) in East Africa. J. Zool. 148(3):289-311.

Kalela, O. 1949. Changes in geographic ranges in the avifauna of northern and central Europe in relation to recent changes in climate. Bird-banding 20(2):77-103.

Kiff, L. 1977. The elusive condors of Baja California. Audubon Imprint 2(3):1-3, 5.

King, J. R. 1973. Energetics of reproduction in birds. Pages 78-107 *in* D. S. Farner, ed. Breeding biology of birds. National Academy of Science, Washington, D. C.

King, J. R., and D. S. Farner. 1961. Energy metabolism, thermoregulation, and body temperature. Pages 215-288 *in* A. J. Marshall, ed. Biology and comparative physiology of birds, Volume II. Academic Press, New York.

Klein, D. R. 1970. Food selection by North American deer and their response to over-utilization of preferred plant species. Pages 25-46 *in* A. Watson, ed. Animal populations in relation to their food resources. Blackwell Scientific Publications, Oxford and Edinburgh.

Kleinstauber, K. 1969. The status of cliff-nesting peregrines in the German Democratic Republic. Pages 209-216 *in* J. J. Hickey, ed. Peregrine falcon populations, their biology and decline. University of Wisconsin Press, Madison.

Koford, C. B. 1953. The California condor. Natl. Audubon Soc., Res. Rep. 4. 154 pp.

Kroeber, A. L. 1925. Handbook of the Indians of California. Smithson. Inst., Bur. Am. Ethnol. Bull. 78. 995 pp.

Lack, D. 1937. A review of bird census work and bird population problems. Ibis, Ser. 14, 1(2):369-395.

Lawrence, R. E. 1893. *Pseudogryphus californianus.* Auk 10(3):300-301.

Leeper, D. R. 1894. The argonauts of 'Forty-nine. J. B. Stoll and Co., South Bend, Indiana. 146 pp.

Lehrman, D. S. 1959. Hormonal response to external stimuli in birds. Ibis 101(4):478-496.

Leopold, A. 1933. Game management. Charles Scribners, New York. 481 pp.

Ligon, J. D. 1967. Relationships of the cathartid vultures. Occas. Pap., Mus. Zool. Univ. Mich. No. 651. 26 pp.

Lint, K. C. 1959. San Diego's Andean condors, a closeup of one of the world's most inaccessible birds. Zoonooz 32(3):3-7.

Lint, K. C. 1960. Notes on breeding Andean condors at San Diego Zoo. Int. Zoo Yearb. 2:82.

Macoun, J., and J. M. Macoun. 1909. Catalogue of Canadian birds. Government Printing Bureau, Ottawa. 761 pp.

MacRoberts, B. R., and M. H. MacRoberts. 1972. Social stimulation of reproduction in herring and lesser black-backed gulls. Ibis 114(4):495-506.

Mallette, R. D. 1970. Operational management plan for the California condor. California Department of Fish and Game. 58 pp.

Marshall, A. J. 1951. Food availability as a timing factor in the sexual cycle of birds. Emu 50(2):267-282.

Marshall, A. J. 1952. Non-breeding among Arctic birds. Ibis 94(2):310-333.

Marshall, A. J. 1961. Breeding seasons and migration. Pages 307-339 in A. J. Marshall, ed. Biology and comparative physiology of birds, Volume II. Academic Press, New York and London.

Martin, P. S. 1967. Prehistoric overkill. Pages 75-120 in P. S. Martin and H. E. Wright, Jr., eds. Pleistocene extinction, the search for a cause. Yale University Press, New Haven and London.

McCoy, J. J. 1963. The fossil avifauna of Itchtucknee River, Florida. Auk 80(3):335-351.

McFarland, L. Z., R. L. Garrett, and J. A. Newell. 1971. Normal eggshells and thin eggshells caused by organochlorine insecticides viewed by a scanning electron microscope. Proceedings of the Scanning Electron Microscope Symposium 4:377-384.

McMillan, I. 1968. Man and the California condor. E. P. Dutton and Co., New York. 191 pp.

McNulty, F. 1966. The whooping crane. E. P. Dutton and Co., New York. 190 pp.

Mehringer, P. J., Jr. 1967. The environment of extinction of the late-Pleistocene megafauna in the arid southwestern United States. Pages 247-266 in P. S. Martin and H. E. Wright Jr., eds. Pleistocene extinction. Yale University Press, New Haven and London.

Memphis State University. 1971. Effects of noise on wildlife and other animals. U.S. Environmental Protection Agency, Washington, D.C. 74 pp.

Miller, A. H. 1942. A California condor bone from the coast of southern Oregon. Murrelet 23(3):77.

Miller, A. H., and H. I. Fisher. 1938. The pterylosis of the California condor. Condor 40(6):248-256.

Miller, A. H., I. McMillan, and E. McMillan. 1965. The current status and welfare of the California condor. Natl. Audubon Soc., Res. Rep. 6. 61 pp.

Miller, L. H. 1910. The condor-like vultures of Rancho La Brea. Univ. Calif. Publ., Bull. Dep. Geol. 6(1):1-19.

Miller, L. H. 1911. Avifauna of the Pleistocene cave deposits of California. Univ. Calif., Bull. Dep. Geol. 6(16):365-400.

Miller, L. H. 1927. Pleistocene fauna and flora. Bird remains. Science 66(1702):155-156.

Miller, L. H. 1931. The California condor in Nevada. Condor 33(1):32.

Miller, L. H. 1943. The Pleistocene birds of San Josecito Cavern, Mexico. Univ. Calif. Publ. Zool. 47(5):143-168.

Miller, L. H. 1957. Bird remains from an Oregon Indian midden. Condor 59(1):59-63.

Miller, L. H. 1960. Bird remains from Rampart Cave, Arizona. Condor 62(1):70; 62(4):298.

Miller, L. H., and I. DeMay. 1942. The fossil birds of California. Univ. Calif. Publ. Zool. 47(4):47-142.

Moll, K. H. 1969. On the osprey situation in the German Democratic Republic. Pages 341-343 in J. J. Hickey, ed. Peregrine falcon populations, their biology and decline. University of Wisconsin Press, Madison.

Nelson, M. W. 1969. The status of the peregrine falcon in the Northwest. Pages 61-72 in J. J. Hickey, ed. Peregrine falcon populations, their biology and decline. University of Wisconsin press, Madison.

Newberry, J. S. 1857. Report upon the zoology of the route. Vol. 6, Part IV, No. 2, in J. S. Newberry, Report on explorations and surveys to ascertain the most practicable and economical route for a railroad from the Mississippi River to the Pacific Ocean. Beverly Tucker, Washington, D.C.

Norris, J. P., Jr. 1926. A catalogue of sets of Accipitres' eggs in the collection of Joseph Parker Norris, Jr. Oologist's Record 6(2):25-41.

Oehme, G. 1969. Population trends of the white-tailed sea eagle in North Germany. Pages 351-352 *in* J. J. Hickey, ed. Peregrine falcon populations, their biology and decline. University of Wisconsin Press, Madison.

Olivares, A. 1963. Se esta extinguiendo el condor en Colombia? Revista de la Acad. Columbiana de Ciencias 12(45):21-28.

Parker, H. 1965. The early Indians of Temecula. Paisano Press Inc., Balboa Island, California. 34 pp.

Palmer, R. S. 1972. Patterns of molting. Pages 65-102 *in* D. S. Farner and J. R. King, eds. Avian biology, Volume II. Academic Press, New York and London.

Parmalee, P. W. 1969. California condor and other birds from Stanton Cave, Arizona. J. Ariz. Acad. Sci. 5(4):204-206.

Peale, T. R. 1957. Diary of Titian Ramsay Peale. Dawson's Book Store, Los Angeles. 85 pp.

Phillips, J. C. 1926. An attempt to list the extinct and vanishing birds of the Western Hemisphere, with some notes on recent status, location of specimens, etc. Int. Ornithol. Congr. 6:503-534.

Portielje, A. F. J. 1949. Premarital behavior in the condor (*Sarcoramphus grypus* L.). Z. Tierpsychol. 20(4):468-473.

Poulsen, H. 1963. On the behavior of the South American condor (*Vultur gryphus* L.). Z. Tierpsychol. 20(4):468-473.

Putnam, R. 1928. The letters of Roselle Putnam. Oreg. Hist. Q. 29(3):242-264.

Reed, G. W., and R. Gaines, eds. 1949. The journals, drawings and other papers of J. Goldsborough Bruff, April 2, 1849-July 20, 1851. Columbia University Press, New York. 794 pp.

Reichel, W. L., E. Cromartie, T. G. Lamont, B. M. Mulhern, and R. M. Prouty. 1969. Pesticide residues in eagles. Pestic. Monit. J. 3(3):142-144.

Reid, H. A. 1895. History of Pasadena. Pasadena History Co., Pasadena. 675 pp.

Ricklefs, R. E. 1973. Patterns of growth in birds. II. Growth rate and mode of development. Ibis 115(2):177-201.

Rieger, S. F. 1973. California condor range land use study. California Department of Fish and Game, Sacramento. 13 pp.

Ridgway, R. 1880. Notes on the American vultures (Sarcorhamphidae), with special reference to their generic nomenclature. Bull. Nuttall Ornithol. Club 5(2):77-84.

Rising, H. 1899. Capture of a California condor. Condor 1(2):25-26.

Robinette, W. L., C. R. Baer, R. E. Pillmore, and C. E. Knittle. 1973. Effects of nutritional change on captive mule deer. J. Wildl. Manage. 37(3):312-326.

Robinson, C. S. 1940. Notes on the California condor, collected on Los Padres National Forest, California. U.S. Forest Service, Santa Barbara. 21 pp.

Scott, C. D. 1936a. Are condors extinct in Lower California? Condor 38(1):41-42.

Scott, C. D. 1936b. Who killed the condor? Nat. Mag. 28(6):368-370.

Scouler, J. 1905. Dr. John Scouler's journal of a voyage to northwest America. Q. Oreg. Hist. Soc. 6(2):276-287.

Security Pacific National Bank. 1970. The Southern California report, a study of growth and economic stature. Economic Research Department, Los Angeles. 160 pp.

Sharma, I. K. 1970. Breeding of the Indian white-backed vulture at Jodhpur. Ostrich 41(3):205-207.

Sharp, C. S. 1918. Concerning a condor. Oologist 35(1):8-11.

Shields, A. M. 1895. Nesting of the California vulture. Nidiologist 2(11):148-150.

Sibley, F. C. 1969. Effects of the Sespe Creek Project on the California condor. U.S. Fish and Wildlife Service, Laurel, Maryland. 19 pp.

Siddon, D. 1967. Perched on the brink of oblivion. Los Angeles Times, West Magazine, 5 March: 27-29.

Slobodkin, L. B. 1961. Growth and regulation of animal populations. Holt, Rinehart and Winston, New York. 184 pp.

Sowls, L. K. 1955. Prairie ducks: a study of their behavior, ecology and management. Stackpole Co., Harrisburg. 193 pp.

Spofford, W. R. 1964. The golden eagle in the Trans-Pecos and Edwards Plateau of Texas. Natl. Audubon Soc., Conserv. Rep. 1. 47 pp.

Stager, K. 1964. The role of olfaction in food location by the turkey vulture (*Cathartes aura*). Los Angeles Cty. Mus. Contrib. Sci. 81:1-63.

Statewide Air Pollution Research Center. 1973. Oxidant air pollution effects on a western coniferous forest ecosystem. Task B report: Historical background and proposed systems study of the San Bernardino Mountain area. University of California, Riverside. 153 pp.

Stephens, F. 1899. Lassoing a California condor. Bull. Cooper Ornithol. Club 1(5):88.

Stewart, G. W. 1908. The condor in the San Joaquin Valley. Condor 10(3):130.

Stickel, L. F. 1969. (Comments in roundtable discussion of pesticide effects on raptor populations.) Page 473 *in* J. J. Hickey, ed. Peregrine falcon populations, their biology and decline. University of Wisconsin Press, Madison.

Stickel, W. H. 1975. Some effects of pollutants in terrestrial ecosystems. Pages 25-69 *in* A. D. McIntyre and C. F. Mills, eds. Ecological toxicology research. Plenum Publications Corp., New York.

Stillman, J. D. B. 1967. The gold rush letters. Lewis Osborne, Palo Alto. 75 pp.

Swann, H. K. 1924. Monograph of the birds of prey. Vol. 1, Part 1. Weldon and Wesley, London. 51 pp.

Taber, R. D., and R. F. Dasmann. 1958. The black-tailed deer in the chaparral. Calif. Dep. Fish Game, Game Bull. 8. 163 pp.

Taylor, A. S. 1859. The great vulture of California. Hutching's Calif. Mag. 3(12):540-543; 4(1):17-22; 4(2):61-64.

Taylor, H. R. 1895. Habits of the California condor. Nidiologist 2(6):73-79.

Todd, F. S. 1974. Maturation and behavior of the California condor at the Los Angeles Zoo. Int. Zoo Yearb. 14:145-147.

Todd, F. S., and N. B. Gale. 1970. Further notes on the California condor at Los Angeles Zoo. Int. Zoo Yearb. 10:15-17.

Tolmie, W. F. 1963. William Fraser Tolmie, physician and fur trader. Mitchell Press Ltd., British Columbia. 413 pp.

Townsend, C. H. 1887. Field-notes on the mammals, birds and reptiles of northern California. Proc. U.S. Natl. Mus. 10:159-241.

Townsend, J. K. 1848. Popular monograph on the accipitrine birds of N.A. — No. II, Californian vulture. Literary Record and J. Linnaean Assoc., Pennsylvania College 4(12):265-272.

Van Velzen, A. C., W. B. Stiles, and L. F. Stickel. 1972. Lethal mobilization of DDT by cowbirds. J. Wildl. Manage. 36(3):733-739.

Vaughan, T. 1971. Russian museums: a unique trip by rail. West. Mus. Q. 7(3):1-7.

Ventura County Planning Department. 1970. Report on grazing land relative to the Land Conservation Act. Ventura, California. 5 pp.

Vernon, C. J. 1965. The 1964 black eagle survey in the Matopos, Rhodesia. Arnoldia 2(6):1-9.

Von Haartman, L. 1972. Influence of territory upon structure and dynamics of bird populations. Pages 101-111 *in* Population ecology of migratory birds: a symposium. U.S. Bur. Sport Fish. Wildl., Wildl. Res. Rep. 2.

Wetmore, A. 1931a. The California condor in New Mexico. Condor 33(2):76-77.

Wetmore, A. 1931b. The avifauna of the Pleistocene in Florida. Smithson. Misc. Collect. 85(2):1-41.

Wetmore, A. 1932. Additional records of birds from cavern deposits in New Mexico. Condor 34(3):141-142.

Wetmore, A., and H. Friedmann. 1933. The California condor in Texas. Condor 35(1):37-38.

White, C. M. 1969. Breeding Alaskan and Arctic migrant populations of the peregrine. Pages 45-51 *in* J. J. Hickey, ed. Peregrine falcon populations, their biology and decline. University of Wisconsin Press, Madison.

Wilbur, S. R. 1973. The California condor in the Pacific Northwest. Auk 90(1):196-198.

Wilbur, S. R. 1975. California condor plumage and molt as field study aids. California Fish and Game 61(3):144-148.

Wilbur, S. R., W. D. Carrier, and J. C. Borneman. 1974. Supplemental feeding program for California condors. J. Wildl. Manage. 38(2):343-346.

Wilcox, A. 1901. California vulture. Am. Ornithology 1(9):164-168.
Willett, G. 1931. The condor in San Benito County, California. Condor 33(1):31.
Wynne-Edwards, V. C. 1962. Animal dispersion in relation to social behavior. Hafner
    Publishing Co., New York. 653 pp.

APPENDIX I

Record of Condor Occurrence, 1966-1976

The following list includes representative records of California condor distribution and numbers during 1966-76. These sightings, plus additional similar records totaling 3,045 observations, are the basis for the range delineations and population estimates in the present report. All these records are regarded as "positive" (i.e., there is little or no chance that they do not represent condors in the numbers and ages listed). An additional 520 sightings, many of which undoubtedly were valid reports, were excluded from the analysis because not enough information was provided, the ability of the observers was unknown to me, or for other reasons. All 3,565 records are on file with the U.S. Fish and Wildlife Service, Patuxent Wildlife Research Center, Laurel, Maryland.

Abbreviations used in the list are: A, adult birds; I, immature plumaged birds (under about 5 years old); U, birds unclassified to age. Initials of regularly cited observers are: KA (Keith Axelson), JB (John Borneman), DC (Dean Carrier), DCo (David Connell), GS (Grace Corlis), HC (Harold Cribbs), EF (Evalyn Farnsworth), RF (Reno Ferrari), WF (Walter Fieguth), HH (Harry Hayden), DM (Don McLean), MM (Monty Montagne), RM (Robert Mallette), DO (Dan O'Connor), CO (Clyde Osborn), RP (Riley Patterson), PR (Pauline Roulier), DS (Dick Smith), FS (Fred Sibley), IS (Ina Singer), MS (Martin Steiginga), MSl (Mike Silbernagle), SS (Sandra Southard), HU (Hazel Upham), NW (Mrs. J. B. Williams), RMW (Russell and Marion Wilson), SW (Sanford Wilbur), and TZ (Tony Zufich).

Santa Clara County

1966, San Jose: 26 Oct., 2A 1I (DM).
1967, San Jose: 10 Nov., 1I (DM).
1968, San Jose: 23 May, 1A (DM); 26 Oct., 2A (DM).
1970, San Jose: 3 Sept., 1A 1I (DM).
1971, Palo Alto: 10-12 Jan., 1I (H. Mundy, W. Anderson).
1971, San Jose: 28 Sept., 1A 2I (DM).
1972, Palo Alto: 4 March, 1A (G. Meyers).
1972, Pacheco Pass: 1 June, 2A 1I (W. Goodloe).

San Benito County

1967, Quien Sabe Ranch: Feb., 1U (G. Haganen).
1968, Call Mountain: 8 Sept., 2A (F. Williamson).

Monterey County

1970, Cone Peak: 25 Oct., 1U (P. Kinder).
1971, Pacific Grove: 28 Jan., 1A (T. Robinson).

1971, Cone Peak: 22 May, 1A (P. Kinder).
1971, Parkfield: 28 Sept., 2A (J. Edwards).
1973, Parkfield: June, 1A (B. Walton).
1975, Hunter-Liggett Military Reservation: 31 March, 1U (L. Sitton)

Kings County

1970, near Avenal: 3 Sept., 2U (J. Traub).

San Luis Obispo County

1966, Lopez Canyon: 7 Feb., 3A (E. Barbere, D. Peton); 21 April, 1A (E. Barbere).
1966, Hi Mountain: 1 March, 1U (R. Stone); 30 Nov., 2A 1I (FS, JB).
1966, Pozo: 15 March, 1A (R. Stone, J. Blake).
1966, Cholame: 9 Sept., 1A (E. McMillan).
1966, Black Mountain: 22 Sept., 1A (V. Livingston).
1967, Garcia Mountain: 10 Jan., 1A 1I (J. Blake); 14 Feb., 1I (J. Blake).
1967, Hi Mountain: 24 May, 1A 1I (FS); 14 Sept., 1I (FS); 11 Oct., 1A (RF).
1967, Lopez Lake: 26 July, 1U (C. Edon).
1968, Beartrap Canyon: 6 March, 2A (FS, E. McMillan).
1968, Pozo: 13 April, 1A (J. Blake); 31 Aug., 1A (H. Martin); 12 Sept., 2A (J. Blake).
1968, La Panza: 3 May, 1A (L. Todd).
1968, Hi Mountain: 31 May, 1A (RF); 16 June, 1I (RF); 30 July, 1A 1I (FS, DC); 17 Oct., 3A 1U (RF, J. Edwards); 20 Oct. 2A 1I (RF); 4 Nov., 2A (RF); 20 Nov., 2A 1I (FS, DC); 10 Dec. 2A 1I (RF).
1969, Lopez Canyon: 29 Jan., 1A (V. Price, B. Doan).
1969, Fitzhugh Ranch, Villa Creek: 1 April, 1I (A. Fitzhugh); 16 April, 1A 1I (L. Fitzhugh).
1969, Cholame: 27 April, 1U (R. Garrett); 22 June, 2U (R. Gilman).
1969, Simmler: 8 May, 1A (RP).
1969, Beartrap Canyon: 18 June, 1A (FS).
1969, Hi Mountain: 12 July, 2A (RF); 1 Aug., 1I (RF); 26 Nov., 2A 1I (RF); 12 Dec., 2A 1I 2U (RF).
1969, Carrizo Plains: 18 Aug., 2A 2I (E. McMillan).
1969, Rocky Butte: 22 Aug., 1A (B. and H. Robe); 22 Sept., 2A (B. and H. Robe).
1969, Black Mountain: 25 Aug., 1A (J. Gregory).
1970, Pozo: 27 Feb., 1A (J. Blake).
1970, Hi Mountain: 13 March, 1A 1I (DC, SW).
1970, Beartrap Canyon: 27 March, 1A 1I (S. and S. Wilbur).
1970, Palo Prieto Canyon: 29 May, 2U (R. Gilman).
1970, Rocky Butte: 10 Aug., 2I (B. and H. Robe).
1970, Cholame: 19 Oct., 1A (G. Tidwell).
1970, Morro Bay: 27 Dec., 1I (J. Edmisten).
1971, Simmler: 3 Jan., 1A (T. Huff); 5 May, 1A (C. Edon).
1971, Garcia Mountain: 7 Jan., 1A (R. Rominger).

1971, Los Machos Hills: 1 March, 2A 1I (W. Baden).
1971, Hi Mountain: 4 Aug., 2A 1I (V. Price); 15 Dec., 1I (J. Sutter).
1971, Rocky Butte: 15 Aug., 1A 2I (H. Robe).
1972, Shandon: 20 March, 2A (E. McMillan).
1972, Elkhorn Valley: 27 April, 1A (R. Thomas).
1972, Branch Mountain: 15-16 Oct., 1A (R. Reghetti, S. Rollins); 28 Oct., 1I (S. and W. Rollins).
1973, Pozo: 2 Feb., 2A (D. Cooper).
1973, Hi Mountain: 28 May, 2A (J. Conway).
1973, Wilcox Canyon: 6 June, 1A (G. Rhoden).
1973, Beartrap Canyon: 23 July, 2A 1I (B. Walton).
1973, Lopez Canyon: 17 Nov., 1A 2U (J. Conway).
1974, Pilitas Mountain: 14 Feb., 4A (C. Koford).
1974, Hi Mountain: 22 Dec., 1I (J. Gabel).
1975, Pozo Station: 8 March, 1U (J. Arnold).
1975, Hi Mountain: 11 July, 2U (A. Sims).
1975, Los Machos Hills: 12 Nov., 1A (J. Arnold).
1976, Carrizo Plains: 10 Jan., 2A 1I (R. Palm).
1976, Temblor Mountains: 8 June, 1A 3U (D. Bowman).

Santa Barbara County

1966, Los Alamos: 12 Jan., 2A (JB).
1966, San Marcos Pass: 6 April, 2A 1I (J. Mills).
1966, Bluff Camp, Buckhorn Road: 21 May, 2A (W. Hansen); 21 Sept., 2A (JB).
1966, Buellton: 31 May, 2A (RP).
1966, Cuyama Peak: 3 June, 1I (B. Hudson); 23 June, 1A (B. Hudson); 13 July, 1I (B. Hudson); 18 Oct., 1A (B. Hudson).
1966, Pendola: 9 June, 1A (B. Harvey).
1966, Manzana Creek: 12-15 June, 1U 4U (F. Winter, J. Lorenzana).
1966, Figueroa Mountain: 3 July, 2A (HH); 30 July, 1I (HH).
1966, Sierra Madre Ridge: 18 Oct., 2A (F. Thayer, DS).
1966, La Carpa Potreros: 15 Dec., 1A 3U (D. Calkins).
1967, Cuyama: 15 Jan., 2A (E. Morris).
1967, Pendola: 18 Feb., 1U (DS).
1967, Sisquoc Condor Sanctuary area: 27 Feb., 2A (DS); 1 March, 2U (DS); 18 Oct., 2A (DS, W. Griffin).
1967, Figueroa Mountain: 24 March, 2A 1U (C. Smith); 9 Oct., 1A (HH); 4 Nov., 2A (B. Schram).
1967, McPherson Peak: 23 July, 1U (L. Jordan).
1967, Monte Arido: 25 Aug., 1A (FS, JB).
1967, Cuyama Peak: 18 Oct., 1A 1I (D. Jorgensen).
1967, Los Olivos: 29 Nov., 2A (DS).
1967, Sierra Madre Ridge: 12 Nov., 2A (R. Dias); 16-17 Nov., 1A (FS); 4 Dec., 2A (R. Dalen).
1968, Montecito Peak: 8 Jan., 1I (M. Sanchez, G. Davidson).
1968, Sisquoc Condor Sanctuary: 7 Feb., 1A (DS); 12 Aug., 2A (R. Dias, A. Simas); 21 Oct., 1I (A. Simas).

1968, Madulce Peak: 23 March, 1I (H. Buck).

1968, Sierra Madre Ridge: 8 May, 2A (DCo, E. Morris); 23 Oct., 2A (DC, DCo).

1968, McPherson Peak: 3 July, 1I (W. Conrad); 24 Oct., 2A (A. Conrad).

1968, Santa Ynez: 30 July, 1A (G. Adams).

1968, Cuyama Peak: 2 Oct., 1A 1I (V. Lacy); 3 Oct., 3A (V. Lacy); 24 Oct., 2I (V. Lacy).

1968, Figueroa Mountain: 29 Oct., 1U (HH); 5 Dec., 2A (HH).

1969, Sisquoc Condor Sanctuary: 10 Jan., 1I (D. Moody, R. Dias); 1 April, 2A (J. Easton); 15 Oct., 2A (DS, R. Dalen).

1969, Madulce Peak: 30 Jan., 1A (D. Enger, J. Oman); 1 June, 1A (W. Hansen).

1969, Figueroa Mountain; 2 Feb., 1A (J. Baker); 21 May, 1I (HH); 12 Aug., 1A (HH); 9 Oct., 1A (HH).

1969, Bluff Camp — Buckhorn Road: 14 May, 2A 2I (B. Doan, T. Thompson); 31 Dec., 3U (R. Talbot, D. Shields).

1969, McPherson Peak: 19 May, 2U (D. Moody).

1969, Santa Barbara Potrero: 7 July, 2A (DCo).

1970, Sierra Madre Ridge: 8 Jan., 2U, (M. Sims); 3 June, 1U (M. Sims); 9 Aug., 1A (M. Sims); 12 Sept., 1A (M. Sims).

1970, Manzana Narrows: 30 Jan., 2A (E. Kynoch).

1970, Los Prietos: 16 March, 2A (R. Calkins).

1970, Sisquoc Sanctuary: 22 March, 1A (D. Thompson); 27 March, 2U (J. Miller).

1970, Figueroa Mountain: 13 Aug., 1U (HH); 10 Nov., 1U (HH); 3 Dec., 1A (W. Stevens).

1970, Buellton: 5 Sept., 1A (J. Sinton).

1971, Los Alamos: 22 Feb., 2U (T. Monighetti).

1971, Sisquoc Condor Sanctuary: 27 April, 3A (M. Sims); 10 May, 2A (W. Alexander); 9 June, 2A (M. Sims).

1971, McPherson Peak: 23 May, 2A (W. Conrad); 14 Aug., 1A (W. Conrad).

1971, Lake Cachuma: 26 Feb., 1A (I. McMillan).

1971, Cuyama Peak: 19 June, 1A (A. Sims); 3 July, 1I (A. Sims); 8 Nov., 2A (A. Sims).

1971, Figueroa Mountain: 23 Oct., 1A (HH).

1972, Madulce Peak: 4 March, 2A (DS, J. Berry).

1972, Sisquoc Sanctuary: 30 March, 1I (A. Sims).

1972, Sierra Madre Ridge: 3 June, 1A 1I (B. Holdridge); 20 Aug., 1A (DS).

1972, Cuyama Peak: 13 Aug., 2A (G. Carpenter); 1 Sept., 1U (G. Carpenter).

1972, Cachuma Mountain: 27 Aug., 2A (P. Flores).

1972, Figueroa Mountain: 27 Dec., 1A (J. Sutter).

1973, Cuyama Peak: 24 June, 1U (D. O'Connor); 19 July, 1I (D. O'Connor); 7 Oct., 1A (D. O'Connor).

1973, Sisquoc Sanctuary: 23 Feb., 1U (DS).

1973, Sierra Madre Ridge: 6 July, 1A (DS).

1973, Figueroa Mountain: 31 Aug., 1A (H. Greiman).

1974, Sisquoc Sanctuary: 12 April, 1A (L. Mansfield).

1974, Cuyama Peak: 30 May, 1I (K. Allen); 12 July, 1A (K. Allen); 7 Oct., 1A (K. Allen).

1974, Bluff Camp — Buckhorn Road: 10 Oct., 1A (DS, L. Kinnear).

1974, Zaca Mountain: 29 Nov., 1A (R. Easton).

1975, Sisquoc Canyon: 16 Feb., 3A (W. Hansen).

1975, West Big Pine: 27 Feb., 2A (MM, DS); 2 April, 3A (MM, DS); 13 May, 3A 1I (MM, DS); 5 June, 3A (DS, SW); 22 July, 2A (MM); 21 Oct., 1A (MM, DS).

1975, Hurricane Deck area: 8 April, 1A (J. Cody).

1975, Cuyama Peak: 27 May, 1U (J. Black); 15 July, 1A (J. Black).

1976, West Big Pine: 9 Jan., 2A (MM, DS); 22 April, 1A (J. Hamber, DS); 15 June, 2A (MM, DS); 13 July, 2A 1I (MM, DS); 18 Nov., 2A 1I (MM, DS).

Ventura County

1966, Topatopa Bluffs: 5 Jan., 2A (JB).

1966, Hopper Canyon area, Sespe Condor Sanctuary: 25 Jan., 9A 1I (JB); 2 Feb., 13A (FS, JB); 10 Feb., 2A 6U (JB, Y. Miller); 12 April, 2A 1I (JB); 17 May, 3A 2I (JB); 19 July, 3A (JB); 19 Oct., 1I (DCo); 24 Dec., 2A 2I (DCo).

1966, Bucksnort area, Sespe Condor Sanctuary: 5 March, 5A 1I (JB, Y. Miller); 17 March, 6A (G. Morgan); 20 April, 6A 1I (Y. Miller); 4 July, 4A (JB); 7 Oct., 2A (JB).

1966, Ozena: 8 Feb., 2I (HU).

1966, Gold Hill: 9 Feb., 2A (JB).

1966, Santa Paula Canyon: 16 Feb., 1A (JB).

1966, Sespe Hot Springs: 22 March, 6A (JB, FS); 4 Oct., 1A (FS).

1966, Mutau Flat: 23 March, 1A (A. West).

1966, Frazier Mountain: 1 April, 1A 1I (V. Osborn); 29 June, 1A 1I (HU); 2 July, 3A 1I (HU); 9 Sept., 5A (HU).

1966, Matilija Creek: 13 May, 1A (S. Flores); 25 Nov., 1A (JB).

1966, Mt. Pinos: 22 July, 8A (RMW); 8 Aug., 16A (RMW); 12 Aug., 21A (JB); 25 Aug., 18A 2I 1U (FS); 3 Sept., 5A 3I (DS).

1966, Thorn Point: 14 Aug., 2A (TZ); 10 Sept., 1A (JB, FS).

1966, Reyes Peak: 18 Nov., 3U (J. Hunter).

1967, Hopper Canyon: 10 Jan., 7A 1I (FS); 23 Jan., 6A 4I (FS); 7 Feb., 6A 2I (JB, FS); 8 March, 9A 1I (DCo); 28 April, 4A 1I (FS, JB); 4 May, 6A 1I (FS); 19 June, 2A 1I (JB); 21 June, 6A (FS); 12 July, 1A (JB, FS); 28 Nov., 5A (FS).

1967, Potrero Seco: 5 Feb., 1A (B. Stone).

1967, Matilija Creek: 8 Feb., 1A 1I (JB, FS); 26 Feb., 3A (J. Lorenzana); 2 March, 2A (FS).

1967, Agua Blanca: 2 March, 8A (JB); 11 May, 2A (FS); 27 Dec., 2A (JB).

1967, Coldwater Canyon — Sespe Creek: 27 March, 2A (FS); 11 May, 1A (FS); 7 Sept., 2A (JB).

1967, Chismahoo area: 18 May, 6A (D. Adams, C. Hall).

1967, Thorn Point: 23 May, 1A (JB); 25 July, 2A 1I (TZ); 16 Aug., 1A (TZ).

1967, Nordhoff Peak: 19 June, 2A (M. Woodmansee).

1967, Reyes Peak: 22 June, 1A (JB); 18 Oct., 2A (J. Doman, G. Durney).

1967, Frazier Mountain: 23 June, 2A (HU); 9 Aug., 3A 2I (HU); 18 Aug., 8A (HU); 11 Oct., 3A (HU).

1967, Mt. Pinos: 8 June, 1A (O. Widmann); 23 July, 7A 2I (B. Watson); 17 Aug., 23A (JB); 19 Aug., 16A 3I (FS, JB); 2 Sept., 3A (B. Watson).

1967, Topatopa Bluffs: 15 Nov., 1A (JB).

1967, Santa Paula Canyon: 5 Dec., 1A (JB).

1968, Lake Piru: 6 Jan., 2A (T. Turner, A. Moreno); 8 April, 4A (A. Moreno).

1968, Matilija Creek: 18 Jan., 1A (JB).

1968, Hopper Canyon: 30 Jan., 3A (FS); 27 March, 6A (JB); 19 April, 3A 1I (G. Roby); 10 May, 3A 1I (FS, JB); 1 July, 1A (FS, DC); 6 Sept., 4A (FS, DC); 15 Oct., 1A 2I (G. Roby).

1968, Bucksnort area: 20 Jan., 4A (Y. Miller); 16 Oct., 4A (O. Widmann, C. Rust); 16 Dec., 6A 1I (JB); 17 Dec., 8A (FS, RM); 20 Dec., 13A (DC).

1968, Reyes Peak: 5 Feb., 1A 1U (M. Faaborg).

1968, South Mountain: 19 Feb., 1A (RP).

1968, Agua Blanca: 23 April, 2A (JB); 17 May, 2A (FS); 20 June, 2A (DC); 25 Nov., 2A (JB).

1968, Big Mountain — Torrey Canyon: May, 1A (D. Partridge).

1968, Mt. Pinos: 14 May, 1A (B. Glading); 6 July, 2A (B. Watson); 13 July, 6A (B. Watson); 10 Aug., 7A 1I (JB); 29 Aug., 10A 2I (FS); 16 Oct., 1A (G. Nixon, A. Fries).

1968, Thorn Point: 21 May, 1A (TZ); 28 May, 2A 1I (FS); 4 July, 2A (TZ); 11 Oct., 1A (TZ).

1968, Frazier Mountain: 5 June, 2A (HU); 17 June, 1I (HU); 1 Sept., 1I (HU); 17 Oct., 3A (HU).

1968, Nordhoff Peak: 7 June, 1I (M. Woodmansee); 9 Sept., 1I (M. Woodmansee).

1968, Santa Paula Canyon: 16 Oct., 1A 1I (L. Fischer).

1968, Hungry Valley: 17 Oct., 4A (D. Beauchamp).

1969, Hopper Canyon: 3 Jan., 4A 1I (JB); 17 Jan., 5A 1I (FS); 23 July, 1A (DC, FS); 22 Oct., 2A (R. Peery, F. Todd).

1969, Bucksnort area: 27 March, 15A 1I (DC); 2 May, 8A (FS); 15 July, 2A (DC, FS).

1969, Agua Blanca: 9 Jan., 6A (JB); 25 March, 3A (DC, JB); 15 Oct., 3A (J. Spruill, C. Rust); 18 Dec., 8A (SW, JB).

1969, Green Cabins, Sespe Creek: 15 Oct., 3A 1I (KA, F. Simas).

1969, Sulfur Mountain (Upper Ojai): 15 Jan., 1A 1I (M. Anderson); 21 Jan., 2A (J. Taft); 4 April, 2A (JB); 16 Aug., 1U (J. Taft).

1969, Simi Valley: 27 Feb., 1A (N. Bean).

1969, Santa Paula Canyon: 14 April, 2A (JB); 20 Nov., 2A (JB); 12 Dec., 2A 1U (JB, SW).

1969, Matilija Creek: 16 April, 1A (DC, FS); 15 Oct., 2U (S. Vehrs).

1969, Reyes Peak: 15 May, 1U (JB); 15 Oct., 1I (W. McGuire, R. Lavender).

1969, Thorn Point: 25 May, 1I (S. Molnar); 29 May, 1A (JB, FS); 11 July, 1A (TZ).

1969, Mt. Pinos: 28 May, 1A (D. Hayden); 13 July, 5U (KA); 24 July, 5A 2I (RMW); 8 Aug., 22A 3I (JB, E. McMillan); 23 Sept., 2A (DC); 15 Oct., 1A 1U (V. and S. Mangold).

1969, Chismahoo — Laguna Ridge: August, 2A (L. Thomas).

1969, Frazier Mountain: 15 Oct., 2A 1I 1U (HU).

1970, Hopper Canyon: 2 Jan., 2A 1U (JB, SW); 30 Jan., 6A (G. Roby); 20 Feb., 6A (JB, SW); 12 Sept., 2A 2I (J. Marquez); 22 Oct., 3A (R. Dalen); 4 Dec., 3A 1I (JB); 23 Dec., 6A 1I (R. Dalen, DCo).

1970, Bucksnort: 27 Jan., 6A 1I (DC, SW); 13 Feb., 5A (JB); 25 May, 4A (JB, DC, SW); 24 Aug., 1A (JB).

1970, Agua Blanca: 3 Sept., 2A (JB).

1970, Moorpark: 17 Jan., 3A (R. May); 28 Jan., 1A (R. May, P. Rains); 3 Feb., 2A (R. May, P. Rains); 2 April, 2A (R. May, P. Rains).

1970, Santa Paula Canyon: 13 Jan., 1A (DC, JB, SW).

1970, Sulfur Mountain: 5 April, 1I (J. Taft).

1970, Thorn Point: 7 April, 1A (JB, SW); 20 June, 1A (R. Albee); 7 Aug., 1A (R. Albee); 17 Sept., 1A (R. Albee).

1970, Reyes Peak: 12 April, 2A 1I (DC); 28 May, 3U (JB, SW).

1970, Mt. Pinos: 14 June, 1A 2I (KA); 4 July, 4A 4U (RMW); 10 Aug., 6U 1I (JB); 11 Aug., 6A (DC); 22 Aug., 4A 2I (SW).

1970, Frazier Mountain: 10 July, 1A (HU); 12 Aug., 1I (HU); 19 Aug., 10A 2I (HU); 21 Oct., 1A (SW, HU).

1971, Hopper Canyon: 26 Nov., 2A (DC); 1 Dec., 4A 2I (SW); 15 Dec., 3A 2I (SW); 17 Dec., 3A 1I (DC).

1971, Bucksnort: 24 Jan., 1A 1I (J. Marquez); 16 Feb., 2A 1I (JB, SW); 26 Feb., 9A (SW, JB); 20 March, 5A 1I 2U (S. and S. Wilbur); 29 April, 1A 2U (SW, S. Rouleau); 14 May, 5A 2I (JB, SW); 4 June, 5A (JB, SW); 3 July, 4A 1I (DC).

1971, Sulfur Mountain: 1 Feb., 2U (J. Taft); 17 Feb., 2A (J. Taft).

1971, Potrero Seco: 1 April, 2U (G. Roby).

1971, Matilija Creek: 6 April, 2U (E. Gregory).

1971, Simi Valley: 2 May, 1U (N. Bean).

1971, Moorpark: 5 May, 1I (SW).

1971, Nordhoff Peak: 15 May, 1A (R. Albee); 19 June, 2A (R. Albee).

1971, Frazier Mountain: 20 June, 1A (HU); 28 July, 2A (HU).

1971, Mt. Pinos: 17 June, 1A (O. Clark); 10 Aug., 1A 1I (JB); 26 Aug., 4A 3U (JB, SW); 15 Sept., 1A (SW).

1971, Reyes Peak: 27 Aug., 1A (JB).

1971, Thorn Point: 12 Sept., 1A (A. Lopez); 15 Nov., 1A (A. Lopez).

1972, Hopper Canyon: 10 Jan., 2A 2I (JB, SW); 3 Feb., 3A 1I (SW); 7 Feb., 4A 2I (DC, F. Todd); 2 March, 5A 1I (SW, JB); 2 April, 4A 2I (DC, SW); 26 May, 6A 2I (JB, SW); 1 June, 5A 1I 3U (SW); 3 Aug., 1A 2I (SW); 21 Sept., 2A (SW); 30 Oct., 1A 1I (SW); 30 Nov., 3A 2I (JB, SW).

1972, Potrero Seco: 25 Jan., 1A (T. Ingersoll).

1972, Santa Paula Canyon: 28 Jan., 3A 2U (D. Campbell, S. Kurcaba).

1972, Matilija Creek: 4 Feb., 1A (DC).

1972, Reyes Peak: 2 May, 1A 1I (D. Schroeder).

1972, Frazier Mountain: 20 Sept., 1A (HU); 15 Oct., 1I (HU).

1972, Mt. Pinos: 18 June, 3A 3U (KA); 15 July, 1A 1I (W. Bremser); 1 Sept., 3A (SW).

1972, Simi Valley: 23 June, 1A 1I (G. Williams); 11 Sept., 2A (D. Hayes).

1973, Hopper Canyon: 20 Jan., 4A (JB); 31 Jan., 6A (SW); 26 Feb., 4A 1I (T. Raley); 4 April, 3A 1I (DC, SW); 2 May, 2A 2I (JB, SW); 3 Oct., 3A (DC, T. Raley); 5 Dec., 5A (JB, SW).

1973, Matilija Creek: 2 Feb., 1A (JB, SW).

1973, Sulfur Mountain: 6 Feb., 2A (J. Taft).

1973, Reyes Peak: 6 April, 1U (SW).

1973, Thorn Point: 10 July, 1A (JB).

1973, Mt. Pinos: 11 July, 2A (SW); 28 July, 1A 2I 2U (KA).

1973, Frazier Mountain: 25 July, 1A (HU).

1974, Hopper Canyon: 23 Jan., 3A (JB, SW); 19 April, 6A 1I (JB); 14 June, 4A (JB); 10 Sept., 1I (D. Moody); 12 Nov., 1A (JB, SW); 27 Dec., 2A (M. Montagne, D. Moody).

1974, Bucksnort: 19 March, 3A (JB, SW).

1974, Sulfur Mountain: 3 March, 1A (J. Taft).

1974, Thorn Point: 31 March, 1A 1I (T. Adams); 28 May, 1A (D. O'Connor); 4 Aug., 1A (D. O'Connor); 10 Oct., 1I (D. O'Connor).

1974, Frazier Mountain: 11 June, 1I (HU); 15 June, 2A (HU); 8 Sept., 3A (HU).

1974, Mt. Pinos: 22 June, 1A (JB); 17 Aug., 2A 1I (JB).

1974, Santa Paula Peak: 26 July, 1U (T. Sarzotti).

1974, Matilija Creek: 16 Aug., 1A (JB).

1974, Nordhoff Peak: 10 Nov., 1U (E. Gregory).

1975, Hopper Canyon area: 21 Jan., 2A (JB); 18 Feb., 2A 1I (B. Whiting); 25 March, 2I (E. Abeyta); 28 April, 1A 2I (MSl); 11 June, 2A (SW); 15 July, 1A (JB).

1975, Lake Piru: 22 Feb., 2A 1I (A. Moreno); 8 March, 7A (A. Moreno); 27 April, 4A 3U (D. Moody, A. Moreno).

1975, Whiteacre Peak: 27 March, 3A 1I (J. Farley); 10 April, 1A (SW); 29 May, 2A (SW); 29 Dec., 1A (SW).

1975, Frazier Mountain: 11 June, 1A (HU); 5 Aug., 3A 1I (HU).

1975, Mt. Pinos: 23 June, 1A (M. Davidson); 23 July, 2A (H. Herbert); 7 Aug., 3A 1I (D. Van Vuren); 16 Aug., 6A (L. Kiff); 7 Sept., 2A (D. Van Vuren).

1975, Thorn Point: 4 July, 1A (J. Black).

1975, Reyes Peak: 8 Aug., 1A (A. Mercado); 3 Sept., 2A 2I (D. Van Vuren).

1975, Sespe Canyon: 25 Sept., 2A (S. Kurcaba).

1976, Hopper Canyon area: 6 Jan., 6A 2I (D. Moody, J. Rangel); 22 Feb., 1A 1I (MSl); 24 Feb., 6A 2I (SW); 26 March, 3A (MSl, SW); 11 June, 1A (MSl); 17 Dec., 3A (SW).

1976, Lake Piru: 7 Jan., 2A (A. Moreno).

1976, Reyes Creek: 24 Jan., 1A (T. Glenn).

1976, Simi Hills: 22 Feb., 1A (B. Margolis).

1976, Matilija Canyon: 23 Feb., 1U (R. Nelson); 1 April, 1A (R. Nelson); 21 Sept., 1A (D. Pacheco).

1976, Whiteacre Peak: 24 March, 4A 1I (MSl, SW); 5 Oct., 2A (JB, SW); 13 Oct., 3A 1I (MSl); 21 Dec., 3A 1I (SW).

1976, Thorn Point: 25 May, 1A (JB, SW); 12 June, 1A (J. Black).

1976, Reyes Peak: 31 May, 1U (S. Kinchloe); 16 July, 1A (JB).

1976, Frazier Mountain: 3 June, 1I (HU)

1976, Mt. Pinos: 19 June, 1A (F. Maupin); 12 Aug., 1A (D. Waite); 29 Aug., 5U 1I (Santa Monica Bay Audubon Society).

Los Angeles County

1967, Piru Creek Gorge: 5 Jan., 1A (FS); 14 April, 2A 1I (FS); 18 May, 2A (FS); 3 Aug., 1I (FS); 12 Oct., 1A 1I (JB, FS).

1967, Gorman: 24 Oct., 1A (JB).

1968, Calabasas: 3 Jan., 1A 1I (R. Woolford).

1968, Piru Gorge: 20 Feb., 1A 1I (JB).

1968, Whitaker Peak: 12 April, 5A (JB).

1968, Agoura: 15 May, 5A, 1I (D. Bafford).

1969, Calabasas: 19 June, 2A (B. McIntosh).

1969, Piru Gorge: 29 Jan., 1U (G. Roby).

1969, Warm Springs Lookout: 18 July, 1I (M. Stahl).

1969, Slide Mountain: 6 Aug., 1A (GC); 5 Sept., 1A (GC); 15 Oct., 2A (GC).

1969, Gorman: 21 Sept., 1A (J. Mills).

1970, Canton Canyon: 26 Jan., 2A (S. Morgan).

1970, Slide Mountain: 26 Feb., 1A (D. Roberts); 31 May, 2A (GC); 22 Aug., 1I (GC); 15 Sept., 4A (GC); 19 Nov., 2A (GC).

1970, Liebre Mountain: 19 April, 3A 2I (J. Damann).

1971, Slide Mountain: 25 Jan., 1A (JB, R. Bishop); 17 March, 1A 1I (M. Faaborg); 5 May, 2A (GC); 28 July, 1I (GC); 25 Oct., 1A (GC); 29 Nov., 3A (GC).

1971, Whitaker Peak area: 21 Aug., 1U (I. McMillan).

1971, Gorman: 3 Nov., 6A (HC).

1972, Slide Mountain: 24 Sept., 1A 1U (L. Forbis); 11 Oct., 1A (L. Forbis).

1972, Quail Lake: 27 Sept., 1A (DC, JB, SW).

1972, Hungry Valley: 17 Sept., 1I (P. Greene).

1973, Slide Mountain: 16 Feb., 1A (JB).

1973, Quail Lake: 30 May, 1A (WF).

1974, Warm Springs Lookout: 11 June, 2I (M. Stahl).

1975, Slide Mountain: 25 May, 1A (DO); 6 June, 4A (DO); 6 July, 2A 1U (DO); 5 Sept., 2A (DO); 15 Oct., 1A (DO); 25 Nov., 2A 1I (JB).

1975, Calabasas area: 20 Aug., 1A (J. Dunn); 6 Dec., 1A (L. Slate).

1975, Red Rock Mountain: 24 Dec., 2A 1I (S. Hoddy).

1976, Slide Mountain: 5 Jan., 1A (DO); 9 Jan., 1I (DO); 22 June, 1A (D. Mark); 24 Sept., 1A (D. Mark).

1976, Gorman: 27 Feb., 1A (A. Jensen).

1976, Liebre Mountain: 1 April, 3A 2I (SW).

1976, Red Rock Mountain: 29 June, 1I (S. Hoddy).

1976, Quail Lake: 5 Dec., 2A (KA).

Kern County

1966, Bear Mountain: 17 May, 1A (J. Mensch).

1966, Grocer Grade: 8 June, 2A (R. Patterson).

1966, Woody — Granite Station: 26 June, 1A (KA); 27 June, 1I (KA); 5 July, 9A 2I (NW).

1966, Tollgate Lookout: 7 July, 1I (PR); 11 July, 1I (PR); 19 Oct., 1I (PR).

1966, Apache Saddle: 26 July, 2A (T. Ingersoll); 28 July, 1A (R. Fischer); 19 Oct., 1A 1I (J. Lane).

1966, San Emigdio Ranch: 2 Sept., 9A (B. Easley).

1966, Mt. Abel: 4-5 Sept., 2A (J. Mills).

1966, Glennville: 12-18 Sept., 1-2 daily (EF).

1966, Tejon Ranch: 24 Sept., 1I (WF); 13 Oct., 2A (WF); 14 Oct., 3A 2I (WF); 19 Oct., 11A 1I (D. Fry, R. Reed); 9 Nov., 11A (E. McMillan).

1967, Tejon Ranch: 18 Jan., 10A (FS, JB); 1 March, 2A (WF); 21 June, 1I (J. Bailey); 29 Aug., 1A 1I 1U (C. Graves); 4 Nov., 5A (WF); 24 Oct., 16A 3I (FS); 30 Dec., 1A (WF, E. Cofer).

1967, Granite Station: 25 Jan., 1A (NW); 9 April, 2A 1I (NW).

1967, Tehachapi: 28 May, 2A (F. Harris).

1967, Bear Mountain: 2 June, 2A (FS); 3 Aug., 8A 2I (L. Bouscal).

1967, Mt. Abel: 19 July, 2A (DS); 24 Nov., 1A (R. Fischer).

1967, Glennville: 11 July, 2A 1I 4U (EF); 26 Aug., 3A (EF); 6 Sept., 2A 2I (EF); 22 Sept., 2I (EF).

1967, Breckenridge Mountain: 6 Sept., 2A (FS).

1967, Tecuya Ridge: 17 Sept., 1I (C. Graves).

1967, Tollgate Lookout: 24 Oct., 1A (PR).

1967, Oak Flat Lookout, Sequoia Natl. Forest: 18 Oct., 2I (J. Koroloff).

1967, San Emigdio Ranch: 18 Oct., 1A 1I (J. Lane, R. Feldman).

1968, Bear Mountain: 8 Jan., 10A 4U (L. Bouscal); 23 Feb., 3A 1I (FS, RM); 8 May, 1A 1U (E. Cofer, G. Franklin); 16 Oct., 1I (RP).

1968, Tejon Ranch: 7 Feb., 2A (E. Cofer, WF); 8 Aug., 1U (DC, FS); 3 Sept., 9A 1I (HC); late Oct., 25U (WF); 17 Oct., 8A (C. Graves, R. Fordice); 24 Oct., 23A 3I (RM, R. Buss).

1968, Kelso Valley: 14 March, 1A (RP).

1968, Caliente: 15 March, 8U (L. Barrett); 28 Oct., 2A (G. Beerline).

1968, Granite Station: 16 April, 2A (NW).

1968, Kern Canyon near Ming Lake: 18 April, 4A (E. Schneegas).

1968, Yeaguas Mountain: 19 June, 1I (J. Edwards).

1968, Glennville: 26 June, 2A (EF); 21 July, 1A (SS); 11 Aug., 1A (EF); 24 Aug., 13A (EF).

1968, Mt. Abel: 13 Aug., 3A 3I (J. Hunter).

1968, Tecuya Ridge: 27 Aug., 1A 1I (D. Roberts).

1968, San Emigdio Ranch: 16 Oct., 5A (J. Lane, D. Partridge).

1969, Glennville: 1 Feb., 1U (R. Shackelford); 24 Aug., 5A (EF); 15 Sept., 2A (EF).

1969, Garces Highway near Highway 65: 12 Feb., 1I (SS).

1969, Mt. Abel: 16 Feb., 1A 1I (D. Taylor).

1969, Tejon Ranch: 3 March, 1U (HC); May, 2A (WF); 15 Oct., 15U (H. Hagen, D. Zeiner); 22 Oct., 6A (RM, J. Reed); 29 Oct., 12U (WF).

1969, Tehachapi: April, 1A (F. Harris).

1969, Bear Mountain: 6 May, 2A (L. Bouscal); 15 Oct., 2A (RP, B. Easley).

1969, Granite Station: 14 June, 1A (NW); 6 Sept., 2A (NW); 11 Sept., 1I (NW).

1969, Tollgate Lookout: 7 Sept., 2A (PR); 15 Oct., 1I 1U (PR).

1969, Santiago Canyon: 2 Aug., 1A (HC, R. Fischer); 15 Oct., 1A (D. Partridge, J. Lane).

1970, Breckenridge Mountain: 8 April, 1A (C. Graves, W. Asserson); 23 May, 1U (G. Payne); 22 Sept., 1A (W. Asserson, R. Thomas).

1970, Granite Station: 1 May, 3A (C. Graves, W. Asserson); 6 Sept., 2A (NW).

1970, Bear Mountain: 8 June, 7A 5I (RP).

1970, Glennville: 24 July, 8A 3I (EF); 4 Aug., 8A 2I (EF); 15 Aug., 4A 2I (EF); 21 Aug., 5A 17U (EF); 3 Sept., 15U (EF); 4 Sept., 3I 10U (EF); 14 Sept., 13U (EF).

1970, Tollgate Lookout: 17 Aug., 1I (PR); 10 Nov., 1A (PR).

1970, Tejon Ranch: 27 Sept., 5A (WF); 12 Oct., 8A (JB); 29 Oct., 9A (D. Beauchamp, C. Graves); 12 Nov., 13A 1I 5U (SW, RM); 29 Dec., 11U (WF).

1970, Woody: 18 Sept., 7A 2I (SS).

1970, San Emigdio Ranch: 21 Oct., 1U (R. Thomas, D. Partridge).

1970, McKittrick Summit: 4 Nov., 1A (K. Jones).

1971, Caliente: 8 Jan., 1A (R. Buss).

1971, Tejon Ranch: 9 Jan., 8A 1I 7U (HC); 27 Jan., 10A 1I (HC); 24 Feb., 4A (SW, RM); 29 Sept., 5A 1I 2U (JB); 7 Oct., 17A 1I (SW); 14 Oct., 8A 6U (R. Beauchamp, R. Fordice); 6 Nov., 7A (D. Kirks).

1971, McKittrick Summit: 13 June, 1A (F. Todd, N. Gale).

1971, Granite Station: 14 March, 2I (Mrs. F. Stockton).

1971, near Arvin: 27 April, 1A 1I (G. King).

1971, Tollgate Lookout: 9 July, 1I (PR); 29 July, 2A (PR); 11 Sept., 1I (IS).

1971, Glennville: 21 Aug., 4A 1I (EF); 31 Aug., 6A 1I (SW); 9 Sept., 12U (EF).

1972, Granite Station: 23 Jan., 1A (EF); 23 June, 2I (NW); 19 Aug., 4A (M. Carver); 30 Sept., 3A 1I (NW).

1972, Blue Mountain: 15 June, 3A (IS); 29 June, 3A 1I (IS); 1 Aug., 1A 2I (IS); 15 Aug., 3A 12U (IS); 18 Sept., 2A 3U (IS).

1972, Glennville: 29 Aug., 9A 1I (SW); 30 Aug., 6A 6U (EF); 2 Sept., 24U (EF).

1972, Tejon Ranch: 31 Aug., 2A 2I (SW); 17 Sept., 1A 1I (R. Reed).; 4 Oct., 5A 1I 1U (JB, SW); 11 Oct., 18A (KA, J. Tarble, K. Stager).

1973, Granite Station: 28 Jan., 1I (M. Carver); 6 Sept., 5A 1I 8U (M. Carver).

1973, Tejon Ranch: 5 March, 2I (WF); 23 March, 7U (WF); 6 Aug., 4A (WF); 7 Oct., 5A 1I 1U (SW, R. Erickson); 25 Oct., 12A 1I (JB, E. McMillan).

1973, Bear Mountain: 4 April, 1I (J. Daum); 19 April, 4A 1I (W. Long, J. Daum); 2 July, 1I (L. Stevens); 13 Oct., 10U (WF).

1973, Glennville: 13 Aug., 4A (E. McMillan); 22 Aug., 7U (EF); 28 Aug., 1I 9U (EF).

1973, Santiago Canyon: 22 Aug., 3A (RP).

1974, Temblor Valley: 20 April, 2A (C. Twisselman).

1974, Glennville: 22 April, 1A (EF).

1974, McKittrick Summit: 8 May, 1A (D. Clark).

1974, Breckenridge Mountain: 25 July, 1U (R. Nelson); 7 Nov., 1I (J. Shryer).

1974, Tejon Ranch: 9 Sept., 5A 1I (WF); 3 Oct., 11A 1I (D. Hartman); 16 Oct., 7A 1I (SW, M. Brayton); 17 Oct., 12 A (L. Kiff, E. Harrison); 14 Nov., 5A 1I 1U (SW, JB).

1974, Granite Station: 23 Sept., 1A (M. Carver).

1974, Cummings Mountain: 29 Sept., 7A 2I (C. Swick).
1974, Santiago Canyon: 17 Oct., 3A (R. Fordice, R. Buss).
1975, Glennville: Aug., 6A 2I (EF).
1975, Granite Station: 9 Sept., 3A 2I (N. Williams).
1975, Tehachapi Pass: 19 Sept., 1A 1U (J. Chattin).
1975, Tejon Ranch: 27 Sept., 6A 2I (JB); 3 Dec., 2A (SW).
1976, Granite Station: 3 Jan., 1I (F. Stockton); 22 June, 1A 2I (F. Stockton).
1976, Tecuya Ridge: 2 June, 2A 1I (R. Long).
1976, Tejon Ranch: 18 June, 2U (H. Einspahr); 26 Sept., 3A (KA); 10 Oct.,
   4A 3U (KA); 14 Oct., 7A 3I (L. Kiff).
1976, Glennville: 21 June, 4A 4I (G. Record); 7 Aug., 1A 1I (EF).

Tulare County

1966, Mule Peak: 15 June, 2A 1I (M. Barkley); 17 June, 1I (M. Barkley).
1966, Cahoon Rock: 20 May, 1U (L. Kilgore, C. Castro).
1966, Blue Ridge: 30 May-23 Aug., almost daily observations, 1-8 birds, including 1-2I (CO); 5 Sept., 1A (CO); 17 Sept., 1U (CO).
1966, Tobias Lookout: 10 Oct., 2A 1I (I. Stephenson); 25 Oct., 2U (I.
   Stephenson).
1966, Milk Ranch Lookout: 19 Oct., 1U (M. Sitton).
1967, White River: 3 Feb., 1U (FS); 22 Dec., 2U (EF).
1967, Blue Ridge: 30 June, 1A 2I (CO); 21 June, 2A (CO); 1 July, 1I 1U (CO);
   14 July, 1A (CO); 28 July, 1A 1U (CO); 7 Aug., 2A 1I (CO); 8 Sept., 1A
   (CO).
1967, Milk Ranch Lookout: 12 Aug., 1A (A. Peterson).
1968, White River: 5 Feb., 1A (SS); 13 Feb., 1A 2U (SS); 11 March, 3U (SS);
   31 May, 1I (SS).
1968, Springville: 1 March, 1U (M. Mires); 25 Aug., 1A (L. Bastian).
1968, Yokohl Valley: 24 March, 2U (M. Mires).
1968, Jordan Peak: 31 May, 2A (W. Beeler).
1968, Blue Ridge: 10 June, 1A (CO); 14 June, 2A (CO); 25 Aug., 2A 1I (CO); 8
   Sept., 1A (CO).
1968, Coldsprings Peak: 11-12 and 17-18 June, 1A each day (FS).
1968, Mule Peak: 7 July, 1A (M. Barkley); 25 Aug., 1A (M. Barkley); 3 Oct.,
   2A (M. Barkley); 17 Oct., 1A (M. Barkley).
1968, Shadequarter Mountain: 16 Aug., 1A (L. Bawden).
1968, Colony Mill Road, Sequoia Natl. Park: 3 Oct., 1I (C. Shaver).
1968, Tobias Peak: 4 Oct., 2A (I. Stephenson); 21 Oct., 1A (I. Stephenson).
1969, Lake Success: 9 March, 2U (M. Mires).
1969, Blue Ridge: 20 May, 1A (FS, DC); 3 June, 2A (CO); 21 June, 5U (MS);
   23 June, 1A 3I (CO); 5 July, 8U (MS); 9 July, 11U (CO); 24 July, 2A 1I
   (CO); 9 Aug., 7U (MS); 29 Aug., 2A 2I (MS); 12 Sept., 1A (MS).
1969, Coldsprings Peak: 25 Sept., 1I (N. Rickert).
1969, near Orange Cove: 29 Sept., 1A (R. Bigard).
1970, California Hot Springs: 7 April, 2I (B. Waldron, N. McDougald).
1970, Blue Ridge: 28 May, 2I (CO); 5 June, 2A 1I (MS); 22 June, 4A (CO, DC,
   SW); 3 July, 3A (MS); 7 July, 4A 1I (CO); 27 July, 1A 1I (MS); 10 Sept., 1I
   (CO).

1970, Mule Peak: 27 May, 2A (E. Schneegas).

1970, White River: 14 June, 1A (SS).

1970, Yokohl Valley: 20 Aug., 2U (S. Stout).

1970, Success Lake: 11 Sept., 1A (L. Eastian).

1970, Milo: 24 Dec., 1A (F. Lilland).

1971, Mule Peak: 15 June, 1A (M. Barkley).

1971, Blue Ridge: 22 June, 1A 1I (SW, CO); 2 July, 1A 1I (CO); 31 July, 2A (MS); 16 Aug., 5A 3U (MS); 27 Aug., 3A 2I (MS); 22 Sept., 2A 1I (CO); 10 Oct., 2A (MS).

1971, Frazier Valley: 11 Sept., 5A (L. Bastian); 15 Sept., 9A 2I (L. Bastian); 22 Sept., 4A 2I (SW).

1971, Park Ridge Lookout, King Canyon Natl. Park: 22 Sept., 2I (M. Sims).

1971, Buck Canyon, Sequoia Natl. Park: 29 Sept., 1I (G. O'Connell).

1972, White River: 30 Jan., 5U (SS); 20 April, 2A (L. Bastian).

1972, Yokohl Valley: 17 March, 2U (H. Ruth).

1972, Mule Peak: 16 May, 2A (M. Barkley).

1972, Blue Ridge: 14 June, 2A 1I (MS); 27 June, 2A 1I (MS); 21 July, 1A 2I (MS).

1973, Springville: 21 May, 1A (J. Probasco, R. Sheldon).

1973, Blue Ridge: 26 June, 3A 2I (MS); 29 July, 3A 3U (MS).

1973, Coldsprings Peak: 15 July, 1I (R. Day).

1973, Needles Lookout: 19 Aug., 1A (A. Fritz).

1974, Springville: 12 May, 3U (H. Miller); 21 Aug., 3A (V. Chapman).

1974, Blue Ridge: 6 June, 2A (MS); 17 Aug., 3A (MS).

1975, Blue Ridge: 5 June, 2A (MS); 11 July, 4A (MS); 14 July, 1I (F. Torreano).

1975, Yokohl Valley: 21 May, 2U (G. Cunningham).

1976, Blue Ridge: 16 June, 2I (F. Torreano); 13 July, 1A (F. Torreano); 15 July, 1I (F. Torreano); 17 Sept., 2A (C. Layton).

1976, Fountain Springs: 4 Dec., 1A (SS); 17 Dec., 1I (SS).

Fresno County

1968, Trimmer: 5 Feb., 2A (V. Murray).

1969, Huntington Lake: August, 1A (W. Cook).

1971, Balch Camp: 25 Feb., 1A 1I (R. Kramer).

San Bernardino County

1967, Deep Creek, San Bernardino Natl. Forest: 22 Aug., 1A (J. Light).

Riverside County

1969, Joshua Tree Natl. Monument: 31 March, 1A (P. Hessler).

APPENDIX II

Removals from the California Condor Population

Museum records and published reports give some indications of the timing and magnitude of losses within the California condor population. The following tables record these losses; however, they do not give a true picture of the actual effects of various mortality factors. For example, only a few Indian-collected birds are listed. Also, many condors were probably shot or otherwise disposed of over the years and no written records exist. Although I have tried to limit the "museum related collecting" to those specimens purposefully acquired by or for museums and other collectors, some birds lost to other causes probably are included. Therefore, the toll of "collecting" is probably overstated, and that of other factors understated.

In the egg records, I have made no attempt to differentiate between the impact of oologists (those with real interest in keeping, cataloging, and studying eggs) and those who collected eggs to sell. Although one might argue that motives make a difference, it seems to me that the second group would not have existed had there not been demand from the first.

As many as 13 museum specimens with incomplete data may duplicate published records for which no existing specimens have been found. Therefore, a minimum of 288 condors and 71 eggs are known removed from the population between 1792 and 1976.

Abbreviations for age are: A, adult; I, immature; and U, unknown. Abbreviations for cause are: S, shooting; MC, museum related collecting; OC, other purposeful capture; AC, accidental trapping; AS, accident or sickness; P, poisoned; and U, unknown.

All specimen locations are in California unless otherwise noted. Abbreviations used in "Reference" are: *NHM*, natural history museum; *NS*, no specimen saved; *SLU*, specimen location unknown; *AMNH*, American Museum of Natural History; *ANSP*, Academy of Natural Sciences, Philadelphia; *BM*, British Museum; *CAS*, California Academy of Sciences; *CFM*, Chicago Field Museum of Natural History; *HMCZ*, Harvard Museum of Comparative Zoology; *LACM*, Los Angeles County Museum; *MVZ*, Museum of Vertebrate Zoology, University of California; *UCLA*, University of California at Los Angeles; *USNM*, U.S. National Museum; *WFVZ*, Western Foundation of Vertebrate Zoology.

Table A-1. Documented Losses of California Condors, 1792-1976.

Date	Location	Age	Sex	Cause	Reference
December 1792	Monterey County	A	U	MC	BM — Type specimen
18 November 1805	Pacific County, Washington	U	U	MC	NS — Lewis and Clark Journals
16 February 1806	Clatsop County, Oregon	A	U	MC	NS — Lewis and Clark Journals
15 March 1806	Clatsop County, Oregon	U	U	S	NS — Gass 1904
15 March 1806	Clatsop County, Oregon	U	U	S	NS — Gass 1904
6 April 1806	Multnomah County, Oregon	U	U	S	NS — Lewis and Clark Journals
September ? 1825	Clark County, Washington	U	U	MC	SLU — Scouler 1905
March 1826	Clark County, Washington	U	U	MC	NS — Douglas 1914
October 1826	Lane County, Oregon	U	U	MC	NS? — Douglas 1914
February 1827	Clark County, Washington	A	U	MC	SLU — Douglas 1829, 1914
1827?	Clark County, Washington	A	U	MC	SLU — Douglas 1829
April 1835	Clackamas County, Oregon	I	U	MC	Townsend 1848, USNM 78005
November? 1836	Monterey County	A	F	MC	Berlin Museum
1840's	Sonoma County	U	U	OC	Leningrad Museum
1840's	Sonoma County	U	U	OC	Leningrad Museum
1841?	Sonoma County?	I	U	MC	Leningrad NHM 1584
1841	Sonoma County?	A	F	MC	Leningrad NHM 1583
1845?	California	A	U	MC	ANSP 148146
1845?	California	A	U	MC	ANSP 148147
8 September 1845	Napa County	U	U	S	NS — Clyman 1926
19 September 1849	Colusa County	A	U	S	NS — Stillman 1967
20 October 1849	Tehama County?	U	U	S	NS — Reed & Gaines 1949
1851?	Lane County, Oregon	U	U	S	NS — Putnam 1928
1853?	Monterey County	A	M	MC	BM
1853?	Monterey County	A	M	MC	BM 1955.6.N.20.135
1855?	California	U	U	MC	CAS — specimen destroyed
26 July 1855	Monterey County	I	F	MC	BM 1955.6.N.20.136
April 1859	Monterey County	I	U	MC	BM

Date	Locality				Reference
Early 1860's?	Monterey County	U	U	OC	BM 1868.12.29.17
1866	Monterey County	I	M	MC	CFM 95160
1867	Monterey County	I	U	MC	Vienna NHM 40862
1872 or 1873	California	I	U	MC	CAS – specimen destroyed
17 June 1875	San Diego County	A	M	MC	CAS skin, MVZ skeleton 23338
1 January 1877	Monterey County	I	M	MC	CAS
2 November 1878	Los Angeles County	U	U	S	NS – Reid 1895
1878?	Tulare County	U	U	S	NS – C. Osborn, pers. comm.
27 January 1880	San Luis Obispo County	A	M	MC	MVZ 23333
May 1880	San Diego County	U	U	S	NS – Cleveland 1902
1882?	Tehama County	U	U	S	NS – Townsend 1887
10 October 1884	Monterey County	A	M	MC	HMCZ 80168
May 1884	Santa Barbara County	U	U	OC	NS? – Reported in *Ventura News* May 23, 1884
February? 1885	Monterey County	I	U	MC	USNM 103375
February 1885	Monterey County	I	U	MC	USNM 17050
February 1885	Monterey County	A	U	MC	USNM 17047
February 1885	Monterey County	I	U	MC	USNM 103065
February 1885	Monterey County	I	U	MC	Skin BM 1888.10.16.156, Skeleton USNM 17049
13 June 1886	Santa Barbara County	A	M	MC	MVZ 23336
2 August 1886	Riverside County	I	U	MC	HMCZ
1887	Baja California	U	U	S	NS – Grinnell 1928
1887	Baja California	U	U	S	NS – Grinnell 1928
1887	Baja California	U	U	S	NS – Grinnell 1928
3 January 1888	San Diego County	A	M	MC	CAS 19001
16 February 1888	San Luis Obispo County	A	M	MC	MVZ 23335
12 March 1888	San Diego County	I	F	MC	HMCZ 214367
11 May 1888	San Diego County	A	M	MC	HMCZ 80166
2 June 1888	San Diego County	A	F	MC	LACM
1888	California	A	U	MC	Milwaukee NHM 457
1888	Monterey County?	A	U	MC	USNM 113663

Table A-1.(Con't.) *Documented Losses of California Condors, 1792-1976.*

Date	Location	Age	Sex	Cause	Reference
10 January 1889	Monterey County	A	M	MC	CFM 130025
July 1889	Santa Barbara County	A	M	MC	AMNH 469948
8 August 1889	San Benito County	A	U	MC	University of Arizona 3993
1889 or 1890	Humboldt County	I	U	MC	Clarke Museum, Eureka, California
1889	Los Angeles County	U	U	OC	SLU – Lawrence 1893
1890	Fresno County	U	U	P	NS – Fry 1926
1890	Fresno County	U	U	P	NS – Fry 1926
1890	Ventura County	A	U	MC	LACM 18877
10 May 1890	Monterey County	U	U	MC	SLU – Davie 1898
13 August 1890	San Diego County	A	M	MC	San Diego NHM
9 December 1890	San Diego County	A	M	MC	AMNH 469945
10 September 1891	San Diego County	A	M	MC	Peabody Museum (Yale) 8526
1892	Humboldt County	A	U	OC	Clarke Museum, Eureka, California
June 1892?	Los Angeles County	A	U	AS	CFM? Lawrence 1893?
1 June 1892	San Luis Obispo County	A	M	MC	BM 1915.7.12.1
8 January 1893	Riverside County	A	U	MC	CAS
1893?	Unknown	U	U	MC	CAS, destroyed by fire
March? 1893	Santa Barbara County	U	U	S	SLU, *Santa Barbara News*, April 12, 1968
20 July 1893	San Diego County	A	F	MC	CAS 44495
August 1893	San Diego County	A	U	MC	USNM 135475
1 January 1894	San Diego County	A	M	MC	CAS 19002
August 1894	Santa Cruz County	U	U	S	NS? Taylor 1895
10 September 1894	San Diego County	A	F	MC	AMNH 469946
25 December 1894	California	A	M	MC	Swedish NHM 16673
20 February 1895	Santa Barbara County	A	M	MC	MVZ 23334
21 April 1895	Los Angeles County	A	M	MC	SLU, Hoffman 1895
23 October 1895	San Diego County	I	M	MC	AMNH 469944
1896?	Santa Barbara County	U	M	U	UCLA 201, partial skeleton

Date	Location				Specimen
3 February 1896	Monterey County	A	M	MC	AMNH 469943
1896?	Monterey County	A	U	MC	Santa Barbara NHM
April 1896	Monterey County	I	U	OC	ANSP 36094
April 1896	Monterey County	I	U	OC	ANSP 62138
1 May 1896	Ventura County	A	F	MC	Royal Ontario Museum 35618
25 June 1896	San Benito County	A	U	MC	Hastings (Nebraska) Museum 3633
7 July 1896	Monterey County	I	U	OC	SLU, Holmes 1897
8 September 1896	San Diego County	A	M	MC	AMNH 469947
15 October 1896	Santa Barbara County	A	F	MC	AMNH 469949
April 1897	Monterey County	A	M	MC	Vienna NHM 50818
10 April 1897	California	I	U	MC	Ohio State University 5623
16 April 1897	Ventura County	I	F	MC	AMNH 469941
1 May 1897	San Luis Obispo County	I	M	MC	Royal Ontario Museum 35617
6 June 1897	San Luis Obispo County	A	M	MC	BM 1939.12.9.3411
8 October 1897	Orange County	I	U	MC	AMNH 469940
20 February 1898	Santa Barbara County	A	U	MC	CAS
March 1898	Monterey County	I	U	MC	HMCZ 80167
March 1898	Monterey County	A	U	MC	USNM 168797
March 1898	Monterey County	I	U	MC	USNM 168798
5 March 1898	Los Angeles County	I	U	AS	LACM 5860
2 May 1898	Santa Barbara County	A	F	MC	Leningrad NHM 133315
May 1898	Monterey County	I	U	MC	USNM 168799
May 1898	Monterey County	I	U	MC	USNM 168800
8 June 1898	Monterey County	A	M	MC	HMCZ 246480
June 1898	Monterey County	I	U	MC	USNM 168801
1898	Kern County	U	U	S	NS, Koford 1953:145
16 June 1898	Monterey County	I	M	MC	HMCZ 80170
25 August 1898	Los Angeles County	A	U	MC	SLU, Rising 1899
25 August 1898	Los Angeles County	I	U	OC	SLU, Rising 1899
November 1898	Monterey County	I	U	MC	Ottawa, National NHM
8 November 1898	Monterey County	I	M	MC	Delaware NHM 5164
1899	San Diego County	U	U	OC	SLU, feather skirt, Koford 1953

Table A-1.(Con't.) Documented Losses of California Condors, 1792-1976.

Date	Location	Age	Sex	Cause	Reference
April 1899	California	A	U	MC	Vienna NHM 64841
1899	California	I	M	MC	St. Gallen (Switzerland) NHM
10 May 1899	San Diego County	A	F	MC	SLU, Finley 1908
24 May 1899	San Diego County	A	M	AS	NS? Stephens 1899
July 1899	California	A	M	MC	St. Gallen (Switzerland) NHM
11 August 1899	Santa Barbara County	A	F	MC	University of Illinois (Urbana) Z-1619
11 August 1899	Santa Barbara County	A	M	MC	University of Illinois Z-522
27 November 1899	Santa Clara County	A	M	MC	AMNH 469942
1900	Ventura County	I	U	OC	USNM 201427
Early 1900's	Tulare County	U	U	S	NS, Stewart 1908
Early 1900's	Tulare County	U	U	S	NS, Stewart 1908
20 April 1900	Santa Barbara County	I	M	MC	HMCZ 324
July 1900	San Diego County	A	U	MC	BM 1939.12.9.3414
10 August 1900	California	A	F	MC	CFM 11249
10 August 1900	California	A	M	MC	Milwaukee Museum 324
15 August 1900	California	A	M	MC	CFM 11248
15 August 1900	California	I	F	MC	Milwaukee Museum 12146
Early 1900's	Marin County	A	U	MC	CFM 39613
1901	San Diego County	I	U	S	SLU, Sharp 1918
1901	Monterey County	I	U	OC	USNM 192532
1901	Ventura County	I	M	OC	USNM 389300
16 January 1901	Los Angeles County	I	F	S	LACM 5829
February 1901	California	A	M	MC	University of Michigan 215,051
3 April 1901	California	A	M	MC	HMCZ 324
1902	Santa Barbara County	A	U	MC	Santa Barbara Museum, destroyed
May 1902	Santa Barbara County	I	F	OC	USNM 188797
December 1902	Santa Barbara County	I	U	MC	AMNH 352007
December 1902	San Luis Obispo County	A	F	MC	AMNH 90572
1903	Ventura County	A	U	MC	University of Michigan

Date	Location				Collection / Reference
1903	Ventura County	I	F	OC	USNM 370997
1903	Ventura County	I	F	OC	Louisiana State University
1903	San Diego County	A	U	MC	San Diego NHM
March 1903	Santa Barbara County	A	M	MC	CAS 25775
March 1903	Santa Barbara County	A	F	MC	CAS 25776
1903	Santa Barbara County	I	M	OC	HMCZ 300353
1904	Los Angeles County	U	U	S	UCLA 1562 (skeleton)
1904?	Los Angeles County	A	U	S	UCLA
20 April 1905	San Bernardino County	A	M	MC	Denver Museum
May 1905?	Monterey County	A	F	MC	AMNH 750092
22 July 1905	Baja California	I	U	MC	USNM 203218
26 July 1905	Baja California	A	F	MC	USNM 203219
26 July 1905	Baja California	I	U	MC	USNM 203217
1906?	Los Angeles County	I	U	MC	Pomona College
17 June 1906	Ventura County	I	F	MC	AMNH 750093
20 January 1907	California	A	M	MC	Linz, Austria, NHM
1 December 1907	Baja California	A	F	MC	Virginia Polytechnic Institute
1907?	Baja California	A	M	MC	WFVZ
7 February 1908	Ventura County	A	F	MC	AMNH 750094
September 1908	Orange County	U	U	U	NS, H. Swarth field notes
31 December 1908	Los Angeles County	I	M	S	MVZ 7857
1909	Ventura County	I	U	OC	SLU, New York Zoo records
1910	California	I	U	OC	University of Iowa NHM
1911	Kern County	U	U	U	UCLA 318 (skeleton)
8 April 1911	Ventura County	I	F	MC	HMCZ 180862
8 April 1911	Ventura County	A	M	MC	UCLA 11036
June 1911	Los Angeles County	I	M	MC	LACM 20962
1912?	Unknown	I	U	MC	MVZ 23337
1912	Ventura County	I	F	S	UCLA 386
1913?	San Luis Obispo County	U	U	U	NS, Koford 1953:142
April 1916	Ventura County	A	F	MC	LACM 1879, Bi 139
2 April 1916	Ventura County	A	M	S	LACM 20963

Table A-1.(Con't.) Documented Losses of California Condors, 1792-1976.

Date	Location	Age	Sex	Cause	Reference
2 April 1916	Ventura County	A	M	MC	AMNH 352005
5 May 1917	Ventura County	I	U	MC	CAS
11 May 1917	Ventura County	A	M	MC	CAS; skeleton UCLA 588
17 May 1917	Ventura County	A	F	MC	CAS; skeleton UCLA 511
June 1917	Monterey County	I	F	OC	CAS 19010
30 May 1920	Ventura County	I	U	MC	LACM 4795, skeleton UCLA 532
30 May 1920	Ventura County	A	M	MC	LACM (4793?)
30 May 1920	Ventura County	A	M	MC	LACM (4794?)
23 October 1923	Ventura County	I	F	OC	LACM 15885
23 October 1923	Ventura County	A	F	MC	LACM 4896
1924?	Santa Barbara County	I	U	AS	NS, Forest Service records
1924	Ventura County	A	F	MC	Denver Museum 19620
1924	Ventura County	A	U	MC	Denver Museum 19621
1924	Ventura County	A	U	MC	Denver Museum
1924	Ventura County	A	M	MC	Denver Museum 19619
1925?	California	A	U	S	San Diego NHM
August 1927	Santa Barbara County	A	U	S	Santa Barbara NHM
July 1929?	Ventura County	I	F	AS	San Diego NHM 18117
1932?	Kern County	U	U	AS	NS, Koford 1953:145
1932	Baja California	U	U	S	NS, Scott 1936a
1932	Baja California	U	U	S	NS, Scott 1936a
1933	Baja California	U	U	S	NS, Scott 1936a
1934?	Ventura County	I	U	AS	Pioneer Museum, Ventura
17 October 1936	Santa Barbara County	A	F	AS	Santa Barbara NHM
17 October 1936	Santa Barbara County	I	M	AS	Santa Barbara NHM, destroyed
December 1936	Ventura County	A	U	U	Santa Barbara NHM
1937?	Kern County	U	U	AT	NS, Howard 1938
1 January 1937	Kern County	A	U	AS	NS, Miller & Fisher 1938
8 October 1938	Santa Barbara County	U	U	U	MVZ 74888 (skeleton)

Date	Locality				Source
1939	Ventura County	U	U	U	NS, Koford 1953:129, 143
2 February 1941	Ventura County	I	U	AS	MVZ 131373
June 1941	Kern County	A	F	U	Fresno State College
1941	Ventura County	I	U	AS	MVZ 120358
1943	Los Angeles County	U	U	S	NS, Department of Fish & Game files
24 August 1944	Kern County	A	U	S	Foster Bighorn Bar, Rio Vista, California; Koford 1953:146
1945	Kern County	A	U	AS	Santa Barbara NHM (skeleton)
20 October 1945	Ventura County	I	U	AS	MVZ 115625
3 March 1946	Ventura County	U	U	U	MVZ 120359
1946	San Luis Obispo County	U	U	U	NS, Miller et al. 1965:55
12 March 1948	Kern County	I	M	AT	LACM Bi 1800
1948	Kern County	U	U	S	NS, Miller et al. 1965:58
1950	San Luis Obispo County	U	U	U	NS, F. C. Sibley notes
28 February 1950	Kern County	A	M	P	USNM 418251
About 1950	California	U	U	AS	NS, Department of Fish & Game files
1950	San Luis Obispo County	A	U	U	NS, F. C. Sibley notes
1952	Kern County	A	U	S	NS, Miller et al. 1965:58
1957	Kern County	U	U	S	NS, Miller et al. 1965:58
About 1958	Kern County	U	U	S	NS, Miller et al. 1965:58
About 1959	Santa Barbara County	A	U	S	MVZ 152977
About 1961	Kern County	U	U	U	NS, Miller et al. 1965:59
About 1961	Kern County	U	U	U	NS, Miller et al. 1965:59
27 June 1960	Ventura County	A	M	U	LACM 36096
August 1960	Ventura County	U	U	U	Fillmore High School (skeleton)
11 August 1960	Kern County	I	U	U	MVZ 151086
Fall 1960	Kern County	U	U	S	NS, Miller et al. 1965:59
23 September 1963	Kern County	A	U	U	MVZ 151087
23 May 1965	Fresno County	I	U	AS	MVZ 156102
August 1965	Kern County	I	U	U	NS, U.S. Forest Service files
December 1965	San Benito County	U	U	U	USNM 489406
27 October 1966	Ventura County	I	U	AS	USNM 489359

Table A-1.(Con't.) *Documented Losses of California Condors, 1792-1976.*

Date	Location	Age	Sex	Cause	Reference
February 1967	Ventura County	I	U	AS	Los Angeles Zoo, alive
Fall 1972	San Luis Obispo County	A	U	U	NS, Wilbur field notes
Fall 1972	San Luis Obispo County	A	U	U	NS, Wilbur field notes
Fall 1974	Kern County	I	U	U	USNM skeleton
Fall 1976	Kern County	A	F	S	USNM

The following specimens have uncertain collection dates, and are referred to the earliest possible time period (e.g., when they were entered in museum collections, when cited in the literature). Some may be specimens that correspond to previously listed records.

Date	Location	Age	Sex	Cause	Reference
Before					
1827	Unknown	A	U	MC	Leiden NHM
1849	California	I	U	MC	ANSP 41
1857	Unknown	A	F	MC	Brussels (Belgium) NHM
1857	Unknown	A	M	MC	Brussels NHM
1856	California?	I	U	MC	Paris NHM
1858	California?	A	U	MC	Paris NHM
1858	California?	A	U	MC	Paris NHM
1884	San Diego County	I	U	OC	LACM partial skin
1887	San Diego County	U	U	S	NS, F. Stephens records
1890	Unknown	I	U	MC	USNM 370921
1894	Unknown	U	U	MC	CAS destroyed
1894	Unknown	U	U	MC	CAS destroyed
1894	Unknown	U	U	MC	CAS destroyed
1894	Unknown	U	U	MC	CAS destroyed
1894	Unknown	U	U	MC	CAS destroyed
1897	Unknown	A	M	MC	Carnegie Museum
1897	Unknown	A	M	MC	Carnegie Museum
1899	Unknown	U	U	MC	ANSP 38325 (skeleton)
1899	Unknown	U	U	MC	ANSP 38326 (skeleton)

Date	Locality				Museum
Before 1899	Unknown	U	U	MC	ANSP 42 (no longer in museum?)
1900	Ventura County	I	U	S	San Bernardino Museum
1904	Unknown	A	M	MC	Gothenburg (Sweden) NHM 4196
1904	Unknown	A	F	MC	Gothenburg NHM 4197
1904	Monterey County	A	U	MC	Geneva (Switzerland) NHM
1906	Unknown	A	U	MC	AMNH
1910	California	A	U	MC	Cincinnati NHM
1914	Unknown	U	U	U	MVZ 23459 (skeleton)
1929	Unknown	A	U	MC	LACM 16713A
1929	Unknown	I	U	MC	LACM 16713
1937	Unknown	I	U	U	Kern County Museum, Bakersfield
1938	Kern County	I	U	S	Bakersfield (California) College
1939	California	I	U	MC	AMNH 45068
1939	California	I	U	MC	AMNH 70298
1939	California	A	U	MC	AMNH
1939	Unknown	A	U	MC	HMCZ
1946	Unknown	A	U	MC	Reading (Pennsylvania) Museum 46-53-1

No collection dates are available for the following specimens. Some are probably specimens that go with mortality records listed above.

Locality				Museum
Unknown	U	U	U	Milwaukee NHM 5764 (skeleton)
Unknown	A	U	MC	Tring (England) Museum
Southern California	A	F	MC	HMCZ 135407
Riverside County	I	M	MC	HMCZ 80169
Unknown	A	U	MC	AMNH 2806
California	U	U	U	USNM 3369 (skeleton)
San Diego County	I	F	MC	Denver NHM 16354
Unknown	A	U	MC	Denver NHM 25546
Unknown	A	U	U	CAS 34590
Unknown	A	U	U	Arthur Bryant collection, Los Angeles
Unknown	A	U	MC	CFM
Baja California	A	U	U	National Museum, Mexico

Table A-1.(Con't.) *Documented Losses of California Condors, 1792-1976.*

Date	Location	Age	Sex	Cause	Reference
	Unknown	A	U	MC	Roger Williams Museum, Providence, Rhode Island
	Unknown	A	U	MC	Roger Williams Museum
	Unknown	U	U	U	LACM Bi-575 (skeleton)
	Unknown	A	U	U	LACM
	Unknown	A	U	MC	LACM
	Unknown	A	U	U	LACM
	Ventura County	U	U	U	LACM Bi-269 (skeleton)
	Unknown	A	U	OC	CAS 34591
	California	A	U	MC	Cincinnati NHM

Table A-2. *Documented Losses of California Condor Eggs, 1859-1943.*[a]

Date	Location	Reference[b]
28 April 1859	Monterey County	BM 1955.5.5
Before 1874	Monterey County	USNM 9983
Before 1880	Monterey County	SLU, formerly ANSP
July 1879	Santa Cruz County	CFM 2909 (part 1)
July 1879	Santa Cruz County	CFM 2902 (part 2)
April 1883	Monterey County	Florida State Museum
April 1883	Monterey County	Florida State Museum
April 1883	Monterey County	Florida State Museum
1886	San Diego County	WFVZ
10 March 1888	Santa Barbara County	Santa Barbara NHM
May 1889	San Luis Obispo County	WFVZ
February 1892 (1895?)	San Diego County	AMNH
25 April 1893	Unknown	Denver NHM
22 April 1895	Monterey County	USNM 29256
16 (25?) April 1895	San Luis Obispo County	SLU, Shields 1895
28 April 1895	Monterey County	USNM 28052
7 April 1896	Monterey County	Peabody Museum (Yale) 4151
21 April 1896	Santa Barbara County	HMCZ 4041, Wilcox 1901
11 March 1897	San Diego County	ANSP
29 April 1897	Santa Barbara County	BM 760, Anonymous 1898
9 March 1898	San Luis Obispo County	SLU, W. L. Chambers correspondence
26 March 1898	San Luis Obispo County	SLU, W. L. Chambers correspondence
3 April 1898	San Luis Obispo County	WFVZ
6 April 1898	San Benito County	SLU, Willett 1931
26 April 1898	San Luis Obispo County	AMNH 8077
17 April 1899	Santa Barbara County	HMCZ 8454
17 February 1900	Monterey County	USNM 29251
19 February 1900	Monterey County	USNM 29254

Table A-2. (Con't.) Documented Losses of California Condor Eggs, 1859-1943.

Date	Location	Reference[b]
4 March 1900	San Diego County	CFM 15033
19 March 1900	Monterey County	SLU, Anonymous 1900
26 March 1900	San Luis Obispo County	CFM 6165, Anonymous 1900
11 April 1900	Los Angeles County	WFVZ
22 April 1900	Monterey County	SLU, Norris 1926
24 April 1900	San Luis Obispo County	SLU, Chambers correspondence
1 March 1901	Monterey County	MVZ
11 April 1901	Santa Barbara County	HMCZ 8455
25 February 1902	San Diego County	SLU, R. Quigley correspondence
9 March 1902	Santa Barbara County	HMCZ 8453
16 March 1902	Monterey County	San Diego NHM 2137
20 March 1902	Santa Barbara County	AMNH 6937
May 1902	Ventura County	SLU, Chambers correspondence
18 May 1902	Santa Barbara County	HMCZ 8451
18 May 1902	Santa Barbara County	SLU, Chambers correspondence
25 May 1902	Ventura County	CFM 16517
11 February 1903	San Luis Obispo County	SLU, Chambers correspondence
25 March 1905	Monterey County	HMCZ 8449
12 April 1905	Monterey County	WFVZ
October 1905	Ventura County	HMCZ 8450
2 April 1906	Ventura County	BM 1941.1.6.761
10 February 1907	Los Angeles County	SLU, Koford 1953:83
27 February 1907?	San Luis Obispo County	SLU, Koford 1953:83
1 March 1908	San Luis Obispo County	R. L. More, Vernon, Texas
12 May 1909	San Luis Obispo County	HMCZ 8447
4 May 1910	Merced (San Benito?) County	Oakland (California) Museum
4 April 1915	Ventura County	CFM 6164
19 March 1916	Ventura County	Denver NHM
20 March 1917	Ventura County	S. Peyton, Fillmore, California

Date	Location	Source
19? April 1917	San Luis Obispo County	University of Puget Sound
23 March 1919	Ventura County	San Bernardino County Museum
12 March 1920	San Luis Obispo County	ANSP 334
28 May 1920	Ventura County	LACM D576
June 1920	Ventura County	SLU, Koford 1953:85
6 March 1921	Ventura County	WFVZ
17 March 1921	Ventura County	SLU, M. C. Badger field notes
1922	Ventura County	Egg broken, NS, Koford 1953:83
1922	Ventura County	SLU, Koford 1953:83
21 April 1922	Ventura County	CAS 3848
16 March 1939	Ventura County	WFVZ
21 March 1943	Ventura County	WFVZ

Data are incomplete for the following eight eggs. Undoubtedly some of them are the same as those labeled "specimen location unknown" above.

Date	Location	Source
Unknown	Unknown	Carnegie Museum
Unknown	Unknown	Delaware NHM
Unknown	Unknown	Delaware NHM
Unknown	Santa Barbara County	CFM 848
Unknown	Santa Barbara County	MVZ 7534
Unknown	Unknown	Santa Barbara NHM
Unknown	Unknown	Zoological Society of Cincinnati

[a] An egg described as collected in Baja California before 1924 (Swann 1924) has not been located. Eggs laid by captive California condors are currently held by WFVZ; Mr. Nelson Hoy, Media, Pennsylvania; Delaware NHM; and USNM (seven eggs). The location of a final egg of the captive condors is unknown.

[b] See Appendix II (page 71) for abbreviations.

Table A-3. Chronological summary of losses of California condors (numbers at left in each hyphenated pair) and condor eggs (numbers at right).

Location of loss	Before 1800	1800-1819	1820-1829	1830-1839	1840-1849	1850-1859	1860-1869	1870-1879	1880-1889	1890-1899
Oregon and Washington	—	5-0	5-0	1-0	—	1-0	—	—	—	—
Baja California	—	—	—	—	5-0	—	—	—	3-0	—
California[a] North of San Francisco	—	—	—	—	—	—	—	—	2-0	1-0
Monterey, Santa Cruz, Santa Clara, San Benito	1-0	—	—	1-0	—	4-1	3-0	1-2	9-3	20-4
San Luis Obispo	—	—	—	—	—	—	—	—	2-1	3-5
Santa Barbara	—	—	—	—	—	—	—	—	3-1	8-3
Ventura	—	—	—	—	—	—	—	—	—	3-0
Los Angeles, Orange, Riverside, and San Bernardino	—	—	—	—	—	—	—	1-0	2-0	7-0
San Diego	—	—	—	—	—	—	—	1-0	5-1	12-2
Kern, Tulare, and Fresno	—	—	—	—	—	—	—	1-0	—	3-0
Unknown	—	—	—	—	4-0	1-0	—	1-0	1-0	6-1
Totals	1-0	5-0	5-0	2-0	9-0	6-1	3-0	5-2	27-6	63-15

Table A-3. (Con't.) *Chronological summary of losses of California condors (numbers at left in each hyphenated pair) and condor eggs (numbers at right).*

Location of loss	Period								Unknown	Total
	1900-1909	1910-1919	1920-1929	1930-1939	1940-1949	1950-1959	1960-1969	1970-1976		
Oregon and Washington	—	—	—	—	—	—	—	—	—	12-0
Baja California	5-0	—	—	3-0	—	—	—	—	1-1	17-1
California[a] North of San Francisco	1-0	—	—	—	—	—	—	—	—	4-0
Monterey, Santa Cruz, Santa Clara, San Benito	2-8	1-1	—	—	—	—	1-0	—	1-2	44-21
San Luis Obispo	1-6	1-1	0-1	—	1-0	2-0	—	2-0	—	12-14
Santa Barbara	7-5	—	2-0	3-0	1-0	1-0	—	—	—	24-9
Ventura	8-4	9-4	10-7	3-1	4-1	—	3-0	—	2-0	42-17
Los Angeles, Orange, Riverside, and San Bernardino	7-2	1-0	—	—	1-0	—	—	—	1-0	20-2
San Diego	3-2	—	—	—	—	—	—	—	4-0	25-5
Kern, Tulare, and Fresno	2-0	1-0	—	3-0	5-0	4-0	8-0	2-0	—	29-0
Unknown	7-0	2-0	1-0	—	—	1-0	—	—	47-0	71-1
Totals	43-27	15-6	13-8	12-1	11-1	8-0	12-0	4-0	56-3	300-70

[a]Counties, unless otherwise indicated.

Table A-4. Causes of loss of California condors.

Period	Cause of loss							Total
	Shooting	Museum related collecting	Other purposeful capture	Accidental trapping	Accident or sickness	Poison	Unknown	
Before 1800		1						1
1800-19	3	2						5
1820-29		5						5
1830-39		2						2
1840-49	3	4	2					9
1850-59	1	5						6
1860-69		2	1					3
1870-79	2	3						5
1880-89	5	20	2					27
1890-99	3	48	6		3	2	1	63
1900-10	7	27	8				1	43
1910-19	2	9	2				2	15
1920-29	2	8	1		2			13
1930-39	3			1	5		3	12
1940-49	3			1	4		3	11
1950-59	2				1	1	4	8
1960-69	1				3		8	12
1970-76	1						3	4
Unknown	3	41	2				10	56
Totals	41	177	24	2	18	3	35	300

APPENDIX III

Unpublished Material on the California Condor

Borneman, J. C. Field notes 1965-1976. Author's files, National Audubon Society, Ventura, California.

Carrier, W. D. Field notes 1971-1973. Copies included in condor research files, U.S. Fish and Wildlife Service, Patuxent Wildlife Research Center.

Chambers, W. L. Correspondence, list of condor eggs in collections. Bancroft Library, Berkeley, California.

Easton, R. E. Miscellaneous notes and letters pertaining to condors in Santa Barbara County. Santa Barbara Museum of Natural History.

Hill, Harold M. Condor trip notes, Los Padres National Forest 1945-1946. Copies in Fish and Wildlife Service condor research files, Ojai, California.

Hill, Herbert. Condor nesting reports 1950-1952, 1955. Los Padres National Forest, Goleta, California.

Koford, C. B. Original field notes on condor research 1939-1941, 1946-1950. Museum of Vertebrate Zoology, Berkeley, California.

McMillan, E. Original field notes on condor research 1963-1964. Museum of Vertebrate Zoology, Berkeley, California.

Mercado, A. Original field notes on condor study, Los Padres National Forest, July-August 1975. Copies included in condor research files, Fish and Wildlife Service, Ojai, California.

Robinson, C. S. Reports and notes 1936-1940. U.S. Forest Service, Los Padres National Forest, Goleta, California.

Scott, C. D. Manuscript (1935, 1945) "Looking for Condors." Huntington Library, San Marino, California.

Sibley, F. C. Original field notes and administrative reports 1966-1969. Fish and Wildlife Service, Patuxent Wildlife Research Center.

Sprunt, A. Report on trip to Sespe Condor Sanctuary, March-April 1961. National Audubon Society, New York.

Todd, F. S. Manuscript (1971) "Notes on the behavior of Topatopa," a captive condor. Author's files, Sea World, San Diego, California.

U.S. Bureau of Land Management. Public hearing record on Sespe Condor Sanctuary withdrawal, 21 August 1950. 3 volumes, 443 pp. Bureau of Land Management, Sacramento, California.

U.S. Forest Service. Condor patrolman reports, Los Padres National Forest, Goleta, California. R. Davis (March 1951); B. F. Dahlen (March-May 1952); W. Kastorff (July-Aug. 1952); W. M. Harper (March 1956-June 1959); J. W. Gaines (July 1959-March 1964); Y. D. Miller (April 1964-April 1966); and D. L. Connell (June 1966-June 1967).

Van Vuren, D. Manuscript "Deer hunters and the California condor: activity patterns and possible conflicts at Mount Pinos and Pine Mountain, Ventura County, California" (1975). Copy plus original field notes from study included in condor research files, U.S. Fish and Wildlife Service, Ojai, California.

Wilbur, S. R. Original field notes and administrative reports 1969-1976. U.S. Fish and Wildlife Service, Patuxent Wildlife Research Center.

Work, T. Condor trip reports, Los Padres National Forest, 1945-1946. Copies with Fish and Wildlife Service condor research files, Ojai, California.

APPENDIX IV

Chronology of Significant Events in California Condor History

1602—First written record of the California condor, Monterey, California (de la Ascension 1928).

1792—First condor known collected, by Archibald Menzies, at Monterey, California; specimen still in British Museum.

1885—Possibly a State of California law passed about this time, indirectly prohibiting or limiting the killing of condors or taking of their eggs (Cooper 1890); no particulars found.

1905—Section 637a, California Fish and Game laws (approved 19 March) prohibited taking of nongame birds, their nests, or eggs without a permit (condor included, but not specifically named). Fish and Game Commission made formal statement concerning prohibition on condor collecting (Anonymous 1905).

1906—W. L. Chambers compiled a list of condor eggs in collections, copy on file at Bancroft Library, Berkeley, California.

1908—Condor shot in Los Angeles County, shooter fined $50 (Grinnell 1909), apparently the only instance of condor killing or egg taking leading to prosecution and conviction.

1917—Illegally captured condor confiscated in Monterey County, but apparently no prosecution (Anonymous 1917).

1937—Sisquoc Condor Sanctuary, including approximately 485 ha (1,200 acres), established by U.S. Forest Service under Regulation T-9.

1939—Carl B. Koford began intensive studies of California condor, sponsored by research fellowship from National Audubon Society.

1901—State of California Legislature enacted "protective laws," protecting all birds of prey except peregrine falcon (*Falco peregrinus*), Cooper's hawk (*Accipiter cooperi*), and sharp-shinned hawk (*Accipiter striatus*).

1940—Cyril S. Robinson, U.S. Forest Service, prepared the first research report on the condor, the result of observations made in 1936-1940 (Robinson 1940).

1941—Harry Harris published a comprehensive historical account of the condor (Harris 1941).

1942—Convention on Nature Protection and Wildlife Preservation in the Western Hemisphere (the "Natural Resources Treaty") recognized the condor as being in serious trouble; no legal status conferred by the treaty.

1947—Sespe Condor Sanctuary, approximately 14,000 ha (35,000 acres), established by U.S. Forest Service under Regulation T-9.

1948—California Condor Advisory Committee established to advise Los Padres National Forest on condor management.

1949—International Technical Conference on the Protection of Nature, Lake Success, New York: 13 world birds, including the condor, recognized as needing emergency help.

1951—Sespe Condor Sanctuary enlarged to 21,450 ha (53,000 acres) by Forest Service; Public Land Order 695 withdrew a portion of the area from appropriation under public land laws, and prohibited surface entry in areas most critical to the condors.

1951—First patrolman (part-time) assigned to Sespe Condor Sanctuary; Forest Service and National Audubon Society shared salary costs.

1952—Sespe Wildlife Sanctuary Management Plan approved.

1953—Publication of Carl B. Koford's research as National Audubon Society Research Report 4.

1953—First legal protection specifically directed to the condor. Section 1179.5, California Fish and Game Code: "It is unlawful to take any condor at any time or in any manner. No provision of this code or any other law shall be construed to authorize the issuance of a permit to take any condor and no such permit heretofore issued shall have any force or effect for any purpose on and after January 15, 1954."

1956—First full-time patrolman (William M. Harper) assigned to Sespe Condor Sanctuary by U.S. Forest Service.

1959—California Fish and Game Code, Section 3511, California condor among those species listed as "fully protected," those that cannot be taken at any time; no authority for issuing any type of permit. Fine of $500 or 6-month jail sentence authorized.

1965—Publication of National Audubon Society Research Report 6, condor status report based on 1963-1964 field work of Ian I. McMillan and Eben McMillan (Miller et al. 1965).

1965—Condor Advisory Committee formalized; task enlarged to one of advising Regional Forester on all condor matters.

1965—Assignment by National Audubon Society of Condor Naturalist (originally "condor warden") John C. Borneman to full-time educational and field study program.

1965—Endangered Wildlife Research Program initiated at Patuxent Wildlife Research Center, U.S. Fish and Wildlife Service; Fred C. Sibley assigned to full-time research on the condor, succeeded in 1969 by Sanford R. Wilbur.

1965—California Senate Bill 261 signed into law, increased penalty for taking a condor to $1,000 and 1 year in jail.

1965—First Cooperative Survey of the California condor, the first attempt at simultaneous observation of condor numbers and distribution.

1966—Formation of Condor Survey Committee to act as technical advisors in condor research and management; name subsequently changed to Condor Technical Committee, then to Condor Recovery Team.

1966—Passage of Endangered Species Preservation Act (80 Stat. 926), directing Secretary of the Interior to develop a register of endangered species, and authorizing expenditure of Land and Water Conservation Fund monies (78 Stat. 897) for endangered species habitat acquisition.

1967—First official list of United States endangered species published by Secretary of the Interior, condor included.

1968—U.S. Forest Service assigned wildlife biologist W. Dean Carrier to condor investigations, position filled until November 1973.

1969—Passage of Endangered Species Conservation Act (Public Law 91-135) prohibited interstate shipment of wildlife taken contrary to State law.

1970—State of California Endangered Species Act passed, condor subsequently (1971) officially listed as "endangered" under State law.

1970—Secretary of Interior took stand against Sespe Water Project because of expected detrimental effects on condor.

1970—California Department of Fish and Game prepared "Operational management plan for the California condor" (Mallette 1970), guidelines for preservation, management, and further research.

1970—Secretary of the Interior placed moratorium on oil and gas leasing in the Sespe Condor Sanctuary.

1970—U.S. Bureau of Land Management placed moratorium on all mineral leasing activities within area delineated as especially important to condor survival.

1971—Forest Service prepared "Habitat management plan for the California condor" (Carrier 1971), specific guidelines for condor preservation on national forest lands.

1971—California Fish and Game Code, Section 3511, amended (Stats. 1970, Ch. 1036) to allow issuance of permits for collecting fully protected species, including condor, when necessary for scientific research.

1971—Acquisition by Nature Conservancy and Forest Service of 65-ha (162-acre) Huff's Hole property, San Luis Obispo County, important for protection of a condor nesting area.

1972—Migratory bird treaty with Mexico (1937 Convention) amended; California condor among species added to protected bird list; first specific Federal protection of the condor.

1972—Firearms closure for Sespe Condor Sanctuary and adjacent condor habitat established by Forest Supervisor, Los Padres National Forest.

1973—California Assembly Bill 15 passed, prohibiting all aircraft flight within 915 m (3,000 feet) of terrain over the Sespe Condor Sanctuary (Fish and Game Code 10501.5).

1973—Passage of Endangered Species Act of 1973 (Public Law 93-205) made taking of any endangered species a violation of Federal law, and strengthened authority and responsibility of all Federal agencies in protecting endangered species and preserving critical habitat.

1973—Acquisition of an important private inholding in the Sespe Condor Sanctuary, the 130-ha (320-acre) Green Cabins parcels, by National Audubon Society.

1975—Acquisition of the 23-ha (58-acre) Coldwater Canyon tract within the Sespe Condor Sanctuary, by California Department of Fish and Game.

1975—Acquisition of 728-ha (1,800-acre) Hopper Mountain National Wild-
     life Refuge by U.S. Fish and Wildlife Service, as protective buffer for
     the Sespe Condor Sanctuary and as condor feeding habitat.
1975—Approval of California Condor Recovery Plan, and formal recognition
     of Condor Recovery Team.

APPENDIX V

An Annotated List of California Condor Literature

Abbott, J. A. 1939. Eggs: $9,000.00 a dozen. Los Angeles Times Magazine, 14 May:14.
A 1922 egg list values condor egg at $750.00.

Advisory Committee on Predator Control. 1972. Predator control — 1971. Report to the Council on Environmental Quality and the Department of the Interior. 207 pp.
Page 86, brief review of condor — predator control relationships; few cases of condor deaths, but "the strong possibility of secondary poisoning."

Ainsworth, E. 1937. Condors come back; expert tells habits. Los Angeles Times, 28 March.
Condors reputedly increasing at rapid rate, no details.

Ainsworth, E., 1954. Condor crusade. Field and Stream 59(2):46-49.
Alleges only about 38 condors in existence, not more than 8 or 10 nesting pairs.

Allen, A. S. 1916. [Cooper Ornithological Society meeting notes.] Condor 18(4):175.
Dr. Evermann saw "half a dozen" condors in Ventura County.

Allen, T. B. 1974. Vanishing wildlife of North America. National Geographic Society, Wash., D.C. 207 pp.
Pages 157-164, summary of recent research and management.

American Ornithologist's Union. 1940. Report of the Committee on Bird Protection, 1939. Auk 57(2):279-291.
Reports 3-year Audubon fellowship study initiated; Sisquoc Condor Sanctuary established, closed to public ingress.

American Ornithologist's Union. 1941. Report of the Committee on Bird Protection, 1940. Auk 58(2):292-298.
Estimated 50 condors in existence; Committee proposed (1) setting aside entire Los Padres National Forest for condor protection, (2) prohibiting all hunting, except for personnel killing deer for condor food, and (3) restoring the mountain lion population on the Forest so that lion kills would be available to condors.

American Ornithologist's Union. 1942. Report of the Committee on Bird Protection, 1941. Auk 59(2):286-299.
Condor population thought to have increased by 10% in past 2 years (C. B. Koford, personal communication).

American Ornithologist's Union. 1943. Report of the Committee on Bird Protection, 1942. Auk 60(1):152-162.
War Department closed entire Los Padres Forest to public entry; condors believed to be increasing and expanding their range; D. D. McLean reputedly saw 80 condors early in 1942.

American Ornithologist's Union. 1944. Report of the Committee on Bird Protection, 1943. Auk 61(4):622-635.
Condors reputedly increased during past year.

American Ornithologist's Union. 1965. Report of the Committee on Bird Protection, 1964. Auk 82(3):490.
Proposed Sierra Madre Ridge Road and Sespe Creek water project viewed as threats to condors.

American Ornithologist's Union. 1971. Report of the Committee on Conservation, 1970-71. Auk 88(4):902-910.
Notes that data on condor status are confusing, population estimates varying from about 30 to more than 60.

Anderson, N. T. 1935. Condors in northern Los Angeles County, California. Condor 37(3):170.
Antelope Valley, 9 August 1934, seven condors feeding on sheep carcass; December 1934-January 1935, four records (one to three condors).

Anonymous. 1854. [Accession notes, 1855.] Proc. Calif. Acad. Sci. 1:70-71.
Condor specimen acquired from W. B. Farwell, no details; condor feathers received from A. C. Taylor, collected "in the vicinity of the Red Woods of Contra Costa."

Anonymous. 1874. [Minutes of 3 March 1873 meeting.] Proc. Calif. Acad. Sci. 5:36-37.
"Mr. Lorquin" described immature condor captured by him, date and place not given.

Anonymous. 1893. Additions to the Museum for the Year 1892. Proc. Calif. Acad. Sci., Ser. 2, 3:379-382.
Academy received a mounted condor specimen from G. E. Colwell of San Francisco.

Anonymous. 1894a. Three thousand bird skins. Nidiologist 2(4):55.
Walter E. Bryant collection, including five condor skins, given to California Academy of Sciences.

Anonymous. 1894b. Notes and news. Nidiologist 2(4):51.
G. F. Breninger reports two condor sightings (one bird each) near Pacheco Pass, Merced County (no date), and three condors in Santa Cruz County "last summer."

Anonymous. 1896. How the condor is captured. Littell's Living Age 209(2709):640.
Dramatic account of a condor being lassoed and captured, no date or location given.

Anonymous. 1898. Notes on the taking of an egg of the California condor. Museum 4(7):103.
Condor egg collected in Santa Barbara County, 29 April 1897.

Anonymous. 1899. [Correspondence from A. F. Redington.] Bull. Cooper Ornithol. Club 1(1):19.
One condor seen at San Marcos Pass, Santa Barbara County; "We can almost guarantee at least the sight of this species in a day's trip down the Santa Ynez range."

Anonymous. 1900a. Two more eggs of California condor. Condor 2(3):60.
H. R. Taylor's collectors secured condor eggs on 19 March 1900 (Monterey Cty.) and 26 March 1900 (San Luis Obispo Cty.); sold to Miss Jean Bell of Pennsylvania.

Anonymous. 1900b. Eggs of the California condor. Osprey 4(9):142.
H. M. Beesley trying to purchase condor egg for Tring (England) Museum; last recorded sale reportedly in 1887. "There are said to be several oologists who are ready to pay $1,000 to $1,200 for an egg."

Anonymous. 1901. [Report of condor death.] Condor 3(3):79.
F. H. Holmes pet condor "Ben Butler" died of undetermined causes after several years captivity.

Anonymous. 1904. Notes and News. Condor 6(3):83.
Trip into western Los Angeles and Ventura counties by Messrs. Lelande and Howard, on which 11 condors were seen simultaneously "and several nesting aeries were located."

Anonymous. 1905. Annual report of the National Association of Audubon Societies for 1905. Bird-lore 7(6):295-350.
Citing California newspaper: "The (California) Fish and Game Commission has announced that no permits will be issued for collecting the California Condor or its eggs for any purpose."

Anonymous. 1906. The California vulture. Birds Nat. 4(5):188.
General compilation.

Anonymous. 1907. An almost extinct bird. N.Y. Zool. Soc. Bull. 24:318-320.
W. L. Finley's condor "General" acquired by New York Zoo.

Anonymous. 1916. List of accessions to the Museum and Library, 1916. Proc. Calif. Acad. Sci., Ser. 4, 6(8-9):246-250.
Presentation to the Academy of two condor specimens collected by E. B. Towns, January 1894, in San Diego County.

Anonymous. 1917. California condor on exhibition in Golden Gate Park, San Francisco, Calif. Fish Game 3(4):176.
Condor lassoed in Monterey County, confiscated and placed on exhibition by Fish and Game Commission.

Anonymous. 1922. Proceedings of the annual meeting, Audubon Association of the Pacific. Gull 4(2):1-2.
C. Littlejohn notes that in San Mateo County and vicinity "Condors were quite common in the early days. Flocks of buzzards would include one condor in twenty birds."

Anonymous. 1926. Bird that lays $1,500 eggs. Lit. Dig. 90(6):48, 52.
Condor "lays an egg valued by museums and collectors at $1,500 to $2,000"; only 50 condors remaining, California Fish and Game Commission records.

Anonymous. 1927. [Editorial on "Bird that lays $1,500 eggs." Anon. 1926.] Condor 29(3):129.
Notes numerous misstatements, and criticizes drawing attention to the value of eggs.

Anonymous. 1928. Pet condor as cute as a canary. Lit. Dig. 97(5):45-46, 48, 50.
Good general account of W. L. Finley's condor "General."

Anonymous. 1929. Youth fights condor to win thousand dollar egg. Pop. Mech. 52(5):708.
Condor egg allegedly collected in Baja California. See Lume 1938.

Anonymous. 1930. Science news: items. Science 71(Suppl. 1840):14.
Condor wing bone found in Conkling Cave, New Mexico.

Anonymous. 1937a. The condor, largest flying bird, faces extinction. Calif.
Conserv. 2(9):5.
Fantastic information: Condor "mates for life and if anything happens to either
one, the survivor never takes another mate . . . lays an average of one egg every
four years . . . The young remain in the nest for more than a year before they can
fly. During that time the eagle is the condor's one and only enemy."

Anonymous. 1937b. Condor upturn. Time 29(15):51.
Sidney Peyton saw 11 condors in Sespe area of Los Padres Forest; his opinion is
that condors are increasing.

Anonymous. 1951a. The condors' last stand. Life 30(15):75-77.
Picture story of condor in Los Padres Forest; one photo shows seven condors at
roost.

Anonymous. 1951b. Frank Arundell, county naturalist, admits with candor
he knows condor. Ventura County News, 18 Janaury:6.
Early-day egg and skin collecting activities reported.

Anonymous. 1953. To catch a condor. Newsweek 41(19):92.
Account of attempts by San Diego Zoo to capture condors for captive propagation.

Anonymous. 1960. [Field observation.] Gull 42(8):56.
One adult condor seen near Lebec, Kern County, 3 May 1960.

Anonymous. 1964a. Last of the shy condors. Life 57(22):75-76.
Picture story.

Anonymous. 1964b. Condor in danger. Defenders Wildl. News Bull. 39(3):9.
"A group of volunteers are forming to patrol their (the condors') roosting, nesting
and feeding areas"; opposition to Sierra Madre Ridge Road proposal.

Anonymous. 1965a. A Topatopa Dam could destroy the condor. Audubon
Leader's Conserv. Guide 6(1):1-2.
Review of the proposed Sespe Water Project.

Anonymous. 1965b. Condor census — "38 probables." Outdoor Calif.
26(11):16.
Results of First Cooperative Condor Survey.

Anonymous. 1965c. Condor population declines from 60 to 40; gunners
blamed. Defenders Wildl. 40(1):61-62.
Review of Miller et al. 1965a.

Anonymous. 1965d. Condor killed. Audubon Leader's Conserv. Guide
6(14):3.
Photo of powerline mortality.

Anonymous. 1966. Wilderness and the condor. Natl. Parks Mag. 40(220):19-
20.
San Rafael Wilderness and the condor.

Anonymous. 1967. Condors may disappear. My Weekly Reader 36(24):1, 4.
Brief children's article.

Anonymous. 1968. The Audubon view — condors, whooping cranes and Audubon policy. Audubon Mag. 70(6):4.
Captive propagation viewed as a research technique and as a "last ditch" effort to preserve a population.

Anonymous. 1973. To save a bird. Aerosp. Saf. 29(9):11.
Plea for pilots to avoid condor nesting areas.

Anonymous. 1974. Condor Fund drive; seeing the California condor. West. Tanager 41(3):1-2.
Where to see condors.

Anonymous. 1976. Second stage of condor breeding program nears completion. Endangered Species Tech. Bull. 1(5):2, 4.
History of Andean condor propagation at Patuxent Wildlife Research Center. Birds captured in 1966-67 all paired, three of four pairs have produced young. Eventually captive-reared condors are to be released to the wild.

Anthony, A. W. 1893. Birds of San Pedro Martir, Lower California. Zoe 4(3):228-247.
Condors seen daily in May 1893, two dead ones found; saw condor quills used for carrying gold dust.

Anthony, A. W. 1895. Birds of San Fernando, Lower California. Auk 12(2):134-143.
One condor found dead; condors unusual in that area.

Arnold, R. 1909. Condors in a flock. Condor 11(3):101.
Eighteen condors seen near McKittrick, Kern County, 1 October 1908; only two or three condors seen by him in that area in 2 years.

Ashworth, C. W. 1929. California condor. Oologist 46(5):65-66.
Four condors seen 6 miles from Ventura, California, 24 March 1929.

Atkinson, B. 1966. Those "Forty dirty birds." Audubon Mag. 68(4):231-237.
Popular account of life history and status.

Atkinson, B. 1972. "40 dirty birds" hold their own but are never safe. Smithsonian 2(12):66-73.
Popular account, well done.

Audubon, J. J. 1839. Ornithological biography. Vol. 5. Adam and Charles Black, Edinburgh. 664 pp.
Pages 240-245, life history notes from various sources.

Audubon, J. W. 1906. Audubon's western journal, 1849-1850. Arthur H. Clark, Cleveland. 249 pp.
Records of condors in San Diego County (November 1849) and San Joaquin Valley, California (November or December 1849, "many"; March-April 1850, several records; thought he saw nests, but record not certain).

Austin, M. 1974. The land of little rain. Reprint of 1903 edition. University of New Mexico Press, Albuquerque. 171 pp.
Undated records of condors at Tejon Ranch and Red Rock Canyon, Kern County.

Baird, S. F., T. M. Brewer, and R. Ridgway. 1874. A history of North American birds. Vol. 3, land birds. Little, Brown and Co., Boston. 560 pp.
Pages 338-343, good compilation from various sources.

Baker, J. H. 1946. Condor research to be resumed. Audubon Mag. 48(1):53-54.
Notes return of C. B. Koford to finish condor studies; lauds national forest fire closure because it reduces public use of condor areas.

Baker, J. H. 1950a. Better protection for the California condor. Audubon Mag. 52(6):348-354.
Recommendation that Department of Interior close Sespe area to mining and mineral leasing.

Baker, J. H. 1950b. Oil and condors don't mix. Audubon Mag. 52(2):120.
Proposes Sespe mining closure.

Baker, J. H. 1951. Condor prospects improve. Audubon Mag. 53(2):122-123.
Passage of Public Land Order 695, and establishment of Sespe Condor Sanctuary; full text of land order.

Baker, J. H. 1953. Threat to the condors. Audubon Mag. 55(2):68.
Protests issuance of permit to San Diego Zoo to trap condors.

Bancroft, H. H. 1882. The native races. Vol. 3, myths and legends. A. L. Bancroft and Co., San Francisco. 796 pp.
Page 134, general comments on American Indian religion and condor; page 168, description of the "panes" festival, involving sacrificing a condor.

Barnes, R. M. 1912. California condor's egg. Oologist 29(5):269.
Condor egg from San Diego County; details in Gedney 1900.

Barnes, R. M. 1913. Condor of United States. Oologist 30(1):13-14.
Quotes fanciful magazine information from Youth's Companion, decries printing of such misinformation in "any reputable publication."

Barnes, R. M. 1931. The California condor. Oologist 48(12):175.
One condor reported from Beverly Hills, Los Angeles County, 11 November 1931.

Beebe, C. W. 1906. The California condor. Bull. Zool. Soc. N.Y. 20:258-259.
Description of live condor in New York Zoo.

Beebe, C. W. 1909. New World vultures. Part II. N.Y. Zool. Soc. Bull. 32:465-470.
Mainly a description of W. L. Finley's condor "General." Beebe adds, "I have carefully tested the (California condor's) power of scent . . . and if present at all it is very slight indeed."

Beebe, C. W., and L. S. Crandall. 1912. The birds of prey and their aviary. Part II. N.Y. Zool. Soc. Bull. 16(52):886-889.
Notes that New York Zoo has three California condors.

Behle, W. H. 1944. Check-list of the birds of Utah. Condor 46(2):67-87.
Condor on State list on basis of one record (Henshaw 1875).

Belding L. 1879. A partial list of the birds of central California. Proc. U.S. Natl. Mus. 1:388-449.
Sacramento Valley, California: condor "very rare," seen occasionally in winter.

Belding, L. 1890. Land birds of the Pacific district. Occas. Pap., Calif. Acad. Sci. 2:1-274.
Summarizes comments of various observers.

Bendire, C. 1892. Life histories of North American birds. Smithson. Inst. Spec. Bull. 1. 446 pp.
Pages 157-161, general comments on life history and status; attributes a major decline to poisoning, but no details given; condors noted as "moderately abundant" in "Tulare" (San Joaquin) Valley, 1866-1868.

Bent, A. C. 1937. Life histories of North American birds of prey. Part I. Bull. U.S. Natl. Mus. 167. 409 pp.
Pages 1-13, general compilation of available data.

Bidwell, J. 1964. A journey to California, 1841. The journal of John Bidwell. Friends of the Bancroft Library, Berkeley. 55 pp.
General comment (no locations given) that both "buzzards" (turkey vultures) and "vultures" (condors) are numerous in California.

Bidwell, J. 1966. Life in California before the Gold Discovery. Lewis Osborne, Palo Alto. 76 pp.
1840's — "New Mexican" miners in Los Angeles County "invariably carried their gold . . . in a large quill — that of a vulture (condor) or turkey buzzard."

Bishop, R. C. 1971. Conservation of the California condor in relation to the proposed phosphate mining and processing operation in Los Padres National Forest. Calif. Agric. Exp. Stn., Contrib. to Proj. 1244. 25 pp.
Economic analysis, concludes that "the public could legitimately question the wisdom of using public land for (a phosphate mine). . . risking an endangered species of international significance in the process . . ."

Blake, C. H. 1955. The wing of Teratornis merriami. Int. Ornithol. Congr. 11:261-263.
Compares flight characteristics of condor with suspected features of Teratornis.

Blake, W. C. 1895. Big price for a bird skin. Nidiologist 2(7):96, 2(8):122.
Condor skin sold for 40 pounds.

Bleitz, D. 1946. Climbing for condors. Pac. Pathways 1(10):37-41.
Visits to a condor nest in Ventura County mountains; nestling found dead, arsenic found during analysis; author surmises chick was fed poisoned meat by parents (but see Koford 1953:130 for another explanation).

Bock, W. 1960. Secondary articulation of the avian mandible. Auk 77(1):19-55.
Includes discussion of Cathartidae, with diagram of condor skull.

Bolander, G. 1934. A rhapsody of raptors. Gull 16(8):1-2.
Seven condors (six adults, one immature) seen in Sespe Canyon, Ventura County, 4 December 1933.

Bolton, H. E. 1927. Fray Juan Crespi, missionary explorer of the Pacific Coast, 1769-1774. University of California Press, Berkeley. 402 pp.
Page 210, description of Indian ritual involving a stuffed bird, apparently a condor.

Borland, H. 1974. Take a long, last look at the condor. Natl. Wildl. 12(3):35-36.
Popular account of condor status, some misinformation.

Borneman, J. C. 1966a. The disappearing condors of Sespe. Mod. Maturity 9(5):44-45.
General account of life history and status.

Borneman, J. C. 1966b. Return of a condor. Audubon Mag. 68(3):154-157.
Condor apparently poisoned by strychnine rehabilitated and returned to the wild.

Borneman, J. C. 1969. California condor preservation program. West. Tanager 35(7):59-60.
General progress report.

Borneman, J. C. 1970a. Condors. West. Tanager 36(7):1.
Condor-golden eagle interactions.

Borneman, J. C. 1970b. California condor newsletter. National Audubon Society, Ventura, Calif. 3 pp.
Progress report on research and management.

Borneman, J. C. 1971. California condor newsletter #2. National Audubon Society, Ventura, Calif. 3 pp.
Progress report.

Borneman, J. C. 1972. California condor newsletter #3. National Audubon Society, Ventura, Calif. 3 pp.
Progress report.

Borneman, J. C. 1973. The condor challenge. West. Tanager 39(11):3.
Changes in habitat affecting condors.

Borneman, J. C. 1974a. California condor newsletter #4. National Audubon Society, Ventura, Calif. 3 pp.
Progress report.

Borneman, J. C. 1974b. The 2:00 o'clock condor. West. Tanager 40(10):3.
Watching condors at Mt. Pinos, Ventura County.

Borneman, J. C. 1975a. California condor newsletter #5. National Audubon Society, Ventura, Calif. 1 p.
Progress report.

Borneman, J. C. 1975b. Improving the odds for survival. West. Tanager 42(2):3.
Progress in land acquisition for condors.

Borneman, J. C. 1976a. California condor newsletter #6. National Audubon Society, Ventura, Calif. 2 pp.
Progress report.

Borneman, J. C. 1976b. The California condor, year of decision. West. Tanager 43(2):3.
Discusses possibility of captive propagation program for condors.

Borneman, J. C. 1976c. The victim. Audubon Imprint (Santa Monica Bay Audubon Society) 1(4):4-5.
Attempted rehabilitation of a condor found with a broken wing, result of gunshot.

Borneman, J. C. 1976d. California condors soaring into opaque clouds. Auk 93(3):636.
Condors reported circling up into opaque stratus clouds, an occurrence seldom reported for vultures.

Brewster, W. 1882. On a collection of birds lately made by Mr. F. Stephens in Arizona. Bull. Nuttall Ornithol. Club 7(2):65-86.
Large vulture seen at Cave Creek, Chiricahua Mountains, 7 March 1881, thought to be a California condor.

Brodkorb, P. 1964. Catalogue of fossil birds. Part 2 (Anseriformes through Galliformes). Bull. Fla. State Mus., Biol. Sci. 8(3):195-335.
Pages 250-258, summary of fossil records of condor.

Brown, H. 1899. The California vulture in Arizona. Auk 16(3):272.
March 1881, describes two birds, possibly condors, seen near Pierce's Ferry, western Arizona; one was shot, measured "more than three gun lengths in the spread of its wings."

Brown, L., and D. Amadon. 1968. Eagles, hawks and falcons of the world. Vol. 1. McGraw-Hill Book Co., New York. 414 pp.
Pages 185-189, general life history summary.

Bryan, M. 1901. A study of the birds of Santiago Canyon. Condor 3(3):81-82.
Orange County, California, condors once plentiful there, but none "for twelve years or more."

Bryant, C. A. 1933. [Comments in Cooper Club meeting notes.] Condor 35(3):131.
Six condors observed in Sespe Canyon, Ventura County, 6 December 1932.

Bryant, W. E. 1889. Catalogue of the birds of Lower California. Proc. Calif. Acad. Sci., Ser. 2, 2:237-320.
Condors reported "several places" in Baja California.

Bryant, W. E. 1891. Andrew Jackson Grayson. Zoe 2(1):34-68.
July 1847, "at least a dozen" condors feeding on a deer carcass, Marin County, California.

Buchheister, C. W. 1965a. Meeting the challenges of the "third wave." Audubon Mag. 67(1):18-19.
National Audubon Society proposals to solve condor problems.

Buchheister, C. W. 1965b. Grave threat to the condor. Audubon Mag. 67(2):82-83.
Adverse report on proposed Sespe Water Project.

Buchheister, C. W. 1965c. Our campaign to save the condor. Audubon Mag. 67(3):180.
Audubon assigned naturalist to condor responsibilities; prepared identification leaflet.

Buchheister, C. W. 1965d. Crucial meeting on the condor. Audubon Mag. 67(5):285.
National Audubon reports against Sespe Creek dam proposal.

Buchheister, C. W. 1965e. Annual condor count planned. Audubon Mag. 67(6):357.
Preparations for annual survey. See Mallette and Borneman 1966 for results.

Buchheister, C. W. 1966. Help for the condor. Audubon Mag. 68(1):5.
Progress report.

Buntin, J. 1975. Effects of land development practices in Kern County upon the California condor. Kern Co. (California) Health Department. 28 pp.
Discusses condor as related to various land development proposals; recommends guidelines for development in condor habitat.

Burroughs, R. D. 1961. The natural history of the Lewis and Clark expedition. Michigan State University Press, East Lansing. 340 pp.
Summarizes 1805-06 records from Columbia River region, Oregon and Washington.

California Condor Recovery Team. 1974. California condor recovery plan. U.S. Fish and Wildlife Service. 74 pp.
Action proposal to maintain a population of at least 50 California condors, well distributed within their 1974 range, with an average annual natality of at least four birds.

California Department of Fish and Game. 1974. At the crossroads. A report on California's endangered and rare fish and wildlife. Sacramento. 112 pp.
Pages 13-14, status summary.

California Department of Fish and Game. 1976. At the crossroads, 1976: a report on California's endangered and rare fish and wildlife. Sacramento. 101 pp.
Pages 6-8, status summary.

Callison, C. H. 1966. Sespe Project setback is condor's reprieve. Audubon Mag. 68(3):161.
Ventura County voters reject water project proposal.

Callison, C. H. 1967. San Rafael and the condors. Audubon Mag. 69(3):57.
Brief history of San Rafael Wilderness hearings.

Cant, G. 1960. Condors rising. Sports Illus. 7(29):W2-W10.
General account of status.

Caras, R. A. 1970a. Source of the thunder. The biography of a California condor. Little, Brown and Co., Boston. 181 pp.
Highly fictionalized account.

Caras, R. A. 1970b. Source of the thunder. Audubon 72(6):82-84, 90-131.
Condensation of Caras 1970a.

Carrier, W. D. 1971. Habitat management plan for the California condor. U.S. Forest Service. 51 pp.
Forest Service guidelines for condor management.

Carrier, W. D. 1973. California condor, situation critical. Am. Hiker, March:32-35.
Summary of status and management.

Carrier, W. D., R. D. Mallette, S. Wilbur, and J. C. Borneman. 1972. California condor surveys, 1971. Calif. Fish Game 58(4):327-328.
Results of 1971 survey attempts.

Carver, M. 1960. [Report on a California condor captured in Kern County, California.] News from the Bird-banders 35(3):34-35.
Condor found with dislocated leg, veterinarian set leg and bird was released. (Bird died according to Miller et al. 1965a.)

Cassin, J. 1849. Special report on state of the Academy ornithological collection. Proc. Acad. Nat. Sci. Phila. 4:256-260.
E. L. Kern collected condors in California in 1845, to be added to the Academy collection.

Cassin, J. 1858. United States exploring expedition during the years 1838-1842 under the command of Charles Wilkes, U.S.N. Vol. VIII. Mammalogy and ornithology. J. B. Lippincott and Co., Philadelphia. 466 pp.
Condors seen on the plains of the Willamette River, Oregon, but "much more numerous in California."

Chambers, W. L. 1915. California condor in Los Angeles County. Condor 17(2):102.
One condor seen near Covina, 16 February 1916; "used to be very common in this range . . . seldom seen now."

Chambers, W. L. 1936. The hunter versus wildlife. Condor 38(5):199-202.
Reports two condors shot and brought to his store.

Chapman, F. M. 1908. Camps and cruises of an ornithologist. Appleton and Co., New York. 432 pp.
Pages 259-266, observations of condors and condor nests in Piru Creek area, Ventura County.

Christy, B. H. 1932. A quest for a condor. Condor 34(1):3-5.
Trip into California mountains resulted in sighting of two adult condors; no dates or places mentioned.

Clark, A. M. 1962. From grove to cove to grove, a brief history of Carpinteria Valley, California. Privately printed. 93 pp.
Fantasy. People of Carpinteria declared war on the condors after one stole a baby; they hunted them until they finally disappeared from the area.

Cleland, R. G. 1957. The place called Sespe, the history of a California ranch. San Marino, California, Huntington Library. 120 pp.
Notes that Chumash Indians in Ventura County used condor feathers in ceremonial costumes.

Clement, R. C. 1965. California condor conservation project. West. Tanager 31(7):62.
National Audubon Society hires condor naturalist.

Clement, R. C. 1966. Dangers of pessimism in conservation. Trans. N. Am. Wildl. Nat. Resour. Conf. 31:378-381.
Uses condor as an example of saving or dooming a species by attitude.

Clement, R. C. 1969. The status of the California condor. Pages 163-169 *in* National Geographic Society Research Report, 1964 Projects.
Summarizes Miller et al. 1965a.

Cleveland, C. 1902. [San Diego Natural History Museum notes.] West. Am. Sci. 12(8):130-134.
Condor shot in Cuyamaca Mountains, San Diego County, presented to Museum 7 May 1880, but no taxidermist in town so the specimen was not saved.

Clyman, J. 1926. James Clyman, his diaries and reminiscences. Calif. Hist. Soc. Q. 6(2):136-137.
Napper Creek (Napa County), California, 16 August 1845, "the royal vulture in greate abundance"; 8 September 1845, killed one "royal vulture."

Cochran, D. M. 1927. California condor. Nat. Mag. 9(6):378.
Observations of condors in National Zoo.

Cohen, D. A. 1897. California department. Osprey 1(11-12):150.
Condor reportedly shot, sold to "a saloon-keeper in a country town for $2.00."

Cohen, D. A. 1898a. California notes. Osprey 2(9):120.
Condor egg reported collected for H. R. Taylor.

Cohen, D. A. 1898b. California notes. Osprey 2(10):135.
Two more condor eggs reported collected.

Cohen, D. A. 1899. Pet California condor. Osprey 3(5):78.
Photo and description of Frank Holmes' pet condor "Ben Butler."

Cohen, N. W. 1951. California condors in Madera County, California. Condor 53(3):158.
Nine condors seen at O'Neals, 30 August 1950.

Cooley, R. A., and G. M. Kohls. 1944. The Argasidae of North America, Central America and Cuba. Am. Midl. Nat., Monogr. 1:1-152.
Argas reflexus, "pigeon tick," collected near condor nests.

Cooper, J. G. 1870. Ornithology of California. Vol. 1, land birds. Welch, Bigelow and Co., Cambridge. 592 pp.
Pages 495-503, compilation of then current fact and misinformation.

Cooper, J. G. 1871. Monterey in the dry season. Am. Nat. 4(12):756-758.
August-September 1861, condor listed as one of "the most characteristic land birds."

Cooper, J. G. 1890. A doomed bird. Zoe 1(8):248-249.
May 1872, Orange County, California: one condor observed, apparently hurt or sick; general comments on apparent decline of the species.

Cooper, J. G., and G. Suckley. 1859. The natural history of Washington Territory. Bailliere Bros., New York. 399 pp.
No positive records of condor during 1853-1854, one possible.

Cooper, T. 1976. Government flimflam threatens the condor. Defenders Wildl. 51(3):204-205.
Rabid criticism of government biologists for not taking a stronger stand against a proposed phosphate mine; collusion suggested.

Coues, E. 1866. List of the birds of Fort Whipple, Arizona. Proc. Acad. Nat. Sci. Phila. 18:39-100.
"Resident in southern Arizona," individual birds reported at Fort Yuma, September 1865.

Coues, E. 1897. The manuscript journals of Alexander Henry and of David Thompson, 1799-1814. Edited by E. Coues. Francis P. Harper, New York. 1027 pp.
January 1814, two records of condors near Portland, Oregon.

Cowles, R. B. 1958. Starving the condors? Calif. Fish Game 44(2):175-181.
Suggests that fire control has indirectly harmed condors by increasing brush cover, decreasing availability of animal carcasses.

Cowles, R. B. 1967. Fire suppression, faunal changes and condor diets. Pages 217-224 in Proceedings of California Tall Timbers Fire Ecology Conference, November 9-10.
Suggests that condors are not getting enough calcium in their diet (small mammals less available as food), so egg production is declining.

Crandall, L. S. 1925. Giant birds of prey. Mentor 13(5):1-12.
Brief popular account of condor included.

Crandall, L. S. 1927. Great birds of prey. N.Y. Zool. Soc. Bull. 30(2):26-47.
Includes two photos of immature condors.

Cruickshank, A. D. 1944. In quest of the condor. Nat. Mag. 37(1):13, 48.
Seeing condors near Fillmore, Ventura County.

Crowe, E. 1957. Men of El Tejon, empire in the Tehachapis. Ward Ritchie Press, Los Angeles. 165 pp.
Pages 101-103, story about capturing a condor.

Curl, A. L. 1958. [Cooper Society meeting notes.] Condor 60(1):72.
D. McLean reports two condors feeding on a dead cow near Mt. Hamilton, Santa Clara County, 15 July 1958.

Daggett, F. S. 1898a. Eagle or vulture? Osprey 2(10):133.
Possible condor near Paso Robles.

Daggett, F. S. 1898b. Capture of a California condor. Osprey 2(10):134.
Immature condor with broken wing found in San Gabriel Canyon, Los Angeles County, 4 March 1898; kept alive, later became museum specimen.

Daggett, F. S. 1901a. Capture of a California condor near Pomona, California. Condor 3(2):48.
Immature condor shot in Los Angeles County, 16 January 1901, brought to Daggett.

Daggett, F. S. 1901b. Summer observations in the southern Sierras. Condor 3(5):117-119.
June 1901, one condor seen near Grapevine, Kern County; local residents reporting seeing "numbers of them" at times.

Daniel, J. W. 1900. A day in Rubio Canyon. Wilson Bull. 32(1):2-4.
One condor seen near Pasadena; no date given.

Daniel, J. W. 1903. National Zoo bird items. Am. Ornithol. 3(7):236-237.
Two condors in National Zoo; photo of immature bird.

Davie, O. 1898. Nests and eggs of North American birds. David McKay, Philadelphia. 509 pp.
Pages 191-194, summary of egg collecting records.

Davis, M. 1946. Morning display of the California condor. Auk 63(1):85.
Describes spread-wing postures of captive condor.

Dawson, W. L. 1923. The birds of California. South Moulton Co., San Diego. 2121 pp.
General account of life history and status; firsthand account of visiting a condor nest.

Dawson, W. L., and J. H. Bowles. 1909. The birds of Washington. Occidental Publishing Co., Seattle. 997 pp.
Condor believed to be a former visitor from the south; no longer seen.

de la Ascension, A. 1928. Father Antonio de la Ascension's account of the voyage of Sebastian Vizcaino. Calif. Hist. Soc. Q. 7(4):295-394.
December 1602, birds that were probably condors seen at Monterey, California; *not* feeding on a whale, as record is often interpreted.

Delaney, J. 1974. Saving the thunderbird. San Jose Mercury-News, California Today Suppl., 15 September:20-21.
Popular status report.

De Lasaux, H. 1954. California condor will soar again. Am. For. 60(3):13, 49.
Popular status report.

De Saussure, R. 1956. Remains of the California condor in Arizona caves. Plateau 29(2):44-45.
Condor bones found in three caves in Grand Canyon area.

De Schauensee, R. M. 1941. Rare and extinct birds in the collection of the Academy of Natural Sciences of Philadelphia. Proc. Acad. Nat. Sci. Phila. 93:281-324.
Four condor specimens.

Devoe, A. 1953. Vanishing giants. American Weekly, 19 July:6-8.
Controversy over San Diego Zoo attempt to capture condors.

Dillard, G. M. 1938. [Letter to the editor.] Calif. Conserv. 3(4):8.
Trip to Sisquoc Falls, September 1889, "20 or 30" condors roosting there.

Dillon, R. 1966. The legend of Grizzly Adams. New York, Coward-McCann, Inc. 223 pp.
May or June 1854, Walker River, Nevada; Adams reportedly shot a condor (may be fictional).

Dixon, J. 1924. California condors breed in captivity. Condor 26(5):192.
Egg laying (none fertile) by condors in National Zoo; bird 12 years old when first egg laid.

Douglas, D. 1829. Observations on the *Vultur Californianus* of Shaw. Vigor's Zool. J. 4(1):328-330.
Observations made in Washington and Oregon as far north as the Canadian border, most common along the lower Columbia River. Famous nonsense about black eggs and nests on ground.

Douglas, D. 1914. Journal kept by David Douglas during his travels in North America, 1823-1827. London, William Wesley and Son. 364 pp.
Condors "plentiful" on Umpqua River, Oregon, 3 October 1823 — nine seen in one flock; winter 1826-1827, lower Columbia River area, many condors seen (two collected), but seldom more than one or two at a time.

Downie, D. 1966. The compleat pilot — try it on quiet wings. Private Pilot Mag. 2(12):21-23, 44.
Condor photographed from a sailplane.

Drury, C. M:, ed. 1957. Diary of Titian Ramsay Peale. Los Angeles, Dawson's Book Store. 85 pp.
Condors seen in Umpqua River area, Oregon, 24 October 1841; condors seen near Mt. Shasta and in northern Sacramento Valley, October 1841.

Dunn, H. H. 1905. The California Vulture. Am. Ornithol. 5(12):289-292.
General account; brief account of visiting condor nests with eggs in Orange and Los Angeles counties.

Dunn, H. H. 1907. How I found the nest of the condor. Am. Boy 8(4):127.
Nest visited in Orange County in late April, about 1904; nestling and two adult condors seen.

Dyer, E. I. 1935. Meeting the condor on its own ground. Condor 37(1):5-11.
Put bait out to attract condors, seven (five adults, two immatures) came to bait; also 1933 report of two condors, Santa Clara County.

Edwards, H. A. 1913. California condor. Oologist 30(5):74.
One condor seen at Eagle Rock, Los Angeles County, 14 February 1913.

Eissler, F. 1964. Condors and wilderness. Sierra Club Bull. 49(3):10-12.
Controversy over Sierra Madre Ridge road proposal.

Elliott, C., ed. 1942. Fading trails, the story of endangered American wildlife. MacMillan Co., New York. 279 pp.
Pages 118-126, popular summary of life history and status.

Emerson, W. O. 1887. Ornithological observations in San Diego County. Bull. Calif. Acad. Sci. 2:419-431.
April 1884, one condor seen, Poway Valley.

Evermann, B. W. 1886a. The yellow-billed magpie. Am. Nat. 20(7):607-611.
Condor feeding on dead pig near Santa Paula, 2 April 1881.

Evermann, B. W. 1886b. A list of the birds observed in Ventura County, California. Auk 3(1):86-94, 3(2):179-186.
Condor listed as "resident."

Evermann, B. W. 1886c. Birds observed in Ventura County, California. Pac. Sci. Mon. 1(8):77-89.
Condor "resident."

Fannin, J. 1897. The California vulture in Alberta. Auk 14(1):89.
Two condors reported near Calgary, 10 September 1896; record disputed.

Farquhar, F. P., ed. 1930. Up and down California in 1860-1864, the journal of William H. Brewer. Yale University Press, New Haven. 601 pp.
Condors reported near Monterey in May 1861, and near Pescadero, Monterey County, in July 1861.

Finley, W. L. 1906. Life history of the California condor. Part I. Condor 8(6):135-142.
Detailed observations at Los Angeles County nest site.

Finley, W. L. 1908a. Life history of the California condor. Part II. Condor 10(1):5-10.
Good compilation of distribution, and egg and skin collecting records.

Finley, W. L. 1908b. Life history of the California condor. Part III. Condor 10(2):59-65.
More observations at Los Angeles County nest.

Finley, W. L. 1908c. Home life of the California condor. Century 75(3):370-380.
Nest observations.

Finley, W. L. 1908d. California condor. Sci. Am. 99(1):7-8.
General life history.

Finley, W. L. 1909. General, a pet California condor. Ctry. Life 16(1):35-38.
Observations of a captive bird.

Finley, W. L. 1910. Life history of the California condor. Condor 12(1):5-11.
Behavior of "General," an immature condor, in captivity.

Finley, W. L., and I. Finley. 1915. Condor as a pet. Bird-lore 17(5):413-419.
"General," the condor.

Finley, W. L., and I. Finley. 1926. Passing of the California condor. Nat. Mag. 8(2):95-99.
Popular account of life history and status.

Fisher, A. K. 1893. Report on the ornithology of the Death Valley expedition of 1891. N. Am. Fauna 7:7-158.
Condor "still tolerably common in certain localities west of the Sierra Nevada"; two possible sightings in Owens Valley.

Fisher, H. I. 1939. Pterylosis of the black vulture. Auk 56(4):407-410.
Feather tracts compared to *Gymnogyps* and other cathartids.

Fisher, H. I. 1942. The pterylosis of the Andean condor. Condor 44(1):30-32.
Compared with other cathartids.

Fisher, H. I. 1943. The pterylosis of the king vulture. Condor 45(2):69-73.
Compared with other cathartids.

Fisher, H. I. 1944. The skulls of the cathartid vultures. Condor 46(6):272-296.
Comparisons of cathartid skulls with other falconiform birds; concludes that Pleistocene and Recent California condors represent different species.

Fisher, H. I. 1945a. Flying ability and the anterior intermuscular line on the coracoid. Auk 62(1):125-129.
Cathartid vultures compared with other birds.

Fisher, H. I. 1945b. Locomotion in the fossil vulture *Teratornis*. Am. Midl. Nat. 33(3):725-742.
Compared to *Gymnogyps*.

Fisher, H. I. 1946. Adaptations and comparative anatomy of the locomotor apparatus of New World vultures. Am. Midl. Nat. 35(3):545-727.
Good discussion of flight, use of legs, etc., by *Gymnogyps* and other American vultures.

Fisher, H. I. 1947. The skeletons of recent and fossil *Gymnogyps*. Pac. Sci. 1(4):227-236.
Significance tests from 34 different measurements and ratios "demonstrate conclusively that we are dealing with two distinct forms."

Fisher, W. K. 1904. California vulture in San Mateo Co., California. Condor 6(2):50.
January 1904, one condor seen near Stanford University.

Fleming, J. H. 1924. The California condor in Washington: another version of an old record. Condor 26(3):111-112.
David Douglas collections, 1827.

Flint, P. 1940. Speaking of wings. Los Angeles Times Sunday Magazine, 29 September:7-8.
Aviation engineers make detailed examinations of condor museum specimens; J. R. Pemberton films condors at a carcass.

Fox, W. W. 1973. Condors. Sci. Dig. 74(1):34-38.
Popular compilation.

Fox, W. W. 1974. Will the condor wander yonder? Westways 66(2):56-58, 68, 70.
Popular compilation.

Frazer, J. G. 1935. The golden bough: a study of magic and religion. The MacMillan Co., New York, 752 pp.
Pages 499-501, sacrificial use of condor by California Indians.

Friedmann, H. 1950. The birds of North and Middle America. Part XI. U.S. Natl. Mus. Bull. 50. 793 pp.
Pages 51-59, description and bibliography.

Friedmann, H., L. Griscom, and R. T. Moore. 1950. Distributional check-list of the birds of Mexico. Pac. Coast Avifauna 29:1-202.
Condor believed extinct in Baja California.

Fry, W. 1926. The California condor — a modern roc. Gull 8(5):1-3.
Two condors presumably killed by eating poisoned sheep carcass, 1890; proposes law to make killing condors, taking condor eggs, or putting out poisoned baits felonies.

Fry, W. 1928. The California condor — a modern roc. Sequoia National Park, Nature Guide Service, Bull. 23. 2 pp.
Fry 1926, plus compilation of records for Sequoia National Park and vicinity.

Gabrielson, I. N., and S. G. Jewett. 1940. Birds of Oregon. Oregon State College, Corvallis. 650 pp.
Summarizes Oregon condor records.

Gailey, J., and N. Boliwig. 1973. Observations on the behavior of the Andean condor (*Vultur gryphus*). Condor 75(1):60-63.
Courtship compared to *Gymnogyps*.

Gale, N. B., and F. S. Todd. 1968. A note on the California condor *Gymnogyps californianus* at Los Angeles Zoo. Int. Zoo Yearb. 8:213.
  Captive immature.

Gallaher, W. 1906. A novel find. Condor 8(2):57.
  November 1905, "dried up" condor egg found in Ventura County.

Gambel, W. 1846. Remarks on the birds observed in upper California. Proc. Acad. Nat. Sci. Phila. 3:44-48.
  General comments on condor, apparently not firsthand.

Gass, P. 1904. Gass's journal of the Lewis and Clark expedition. Reprint of edition of 1811. A. C. McClurg and Co., Chicago. 298 pp.
  Condor records along Columbia River, 1806.

Gedney, P. L. 1900. Nesting of the condor on the slope of the Cuyamacas, San Diego Co., Cal. Condor 2(6):124-126.
  Condor egg taken from Boulder Creek area.

Gifford, E. W. 1926. Miwok cults. Univ. Calif. Publ. Am. Archeol. Ethnol. 18(3):391-408.
  Condor (moluku) important "bird chief," used in Miwok ceremonies.

Gifford, E. W. 1932. The Northfork Mono. Univ. Calif. Publ. Am. Archeol. Ethnol. 31(2):15-65.
  Condor (nuniyot) reputed to carry off sleeping people.

Gifford, E. W. 1955. Central Miwok ceremonies. Univ. Calif. Anthropol. Rec. 14(4):261-318.
  Description of moluku dance, celebrating the killing of a condor.

Gifford, E. W., and G. H. Block. 1930. California Indian nights entertainments. Arthur H. Clark Co., Glendale. 323 pp.
  Condor a good character in myths of Humboldt County (Wiyot) Indians, a bad character in Madera County (Western Mono) myth.

Gilbert, B. 1967. A close look at wildlife in America. Saturday Evening Post 240(18):32-48.
  Condor included in popular account.

Gilman, M. F. 1907. Measuring a condor. Condor 9(4):106-108.
  Records of 2 condors shot in San Diego County, 1900-1901; 1888, 14 condors seen in San Bernardino County; two presumed nest sites in San Jacinto Mountain area, Riverside County.

Goddard, P. E. 1929. The Bear River dialect of Athapascan. Univ. Calif. Publ. Am. Archeol. Ethnol. 24(5):291-324.
  Humboldt County Indians may have had a name for the condor — yondiyauw = eats whale.

Goldman, E. W. 1951. Biological investigations in Mexico. Smithsonian Institution, Washington, D.C. 476 pp.
  July 1905, Sierra San Pedro Martir, Baja California: condors "rather common," saw about a dozen on a burro carcass, collected one.

Gray, G. R. 1844. List of the specimens of birds in the collection of the British Museum. Part I — Accipiters. London. 209 pp.
  One condor specimen (the type specimen).

Greene, C., and J. Olsen. 1941. Meet the giant California condor, the world's largest bird. Man to Man 17:38-39, 78-79.
Highly popularized account of condor observations.

Greene, E. R. 1966. A lifetime with the birds: an ornithological logbook. Edwards Bros. Inc., Ann Arbor. 404 pp.
Observations of condors in the Sespe area, 1949-1958.

Greenway, J. C., Jr. 1958. Extinct and vanishing birds of the world. American Committee for International Wildlife Protection, New York. 518 pp.
General summary of life history and status.

Grinnell, J. 1898. Birds of the Pacific slope of Los Angeles County. Pasadena Acad. Sci. Publ. 2. 52 pp.
Condor "tolerably common" and "not by any means becoming extinct."

Grinnell, J. 1905a. Old Fort Tejon. Condor 7(1):9-13.
July 1904, Kern County, saw two condors, others reported them common in the vicinity.

Grinnell, J. 1905b. Summer birds of Mt. Pinos, California. Auk 22(4):378-391.
Late June 1904, saw single condors twice; local residents said condors were common.

Grinnell, J. 1909. Editorial notes and news. Condor 11(3):104.
Immature condor shot at Los Angeles County nest site, shooter fined $50.

Grinnell, J. 1915. A distributional list of the birds of California. Pac. Coast Avifauna 11. 217 pp.
Condor distribution summarized.

Grinnell, J. 1928. A distributional summation of the ornithology of Lower California. Univ. Calif. Publ. Zool. 32(1):1-300.
Condor records in Baja California summarized.

Grinnell, J. 1932a. Type localities of birds described from California. Univ. Calif. Publ. Zool. 38(3):243-324.
Condor type in British Museum, probably collected near Monterey, California, in late 1792 or early 1793.

Grinnell, J. 1932b. Archibald Menzies, first collector of California birds. Condor 34(6):243-252.
Description of condor type specimen.

Grinnell, J., J. Dixon, and J. M. Linsdale. 1930. Vertebrate natural history of a section of northern California through Lassen Peak. University of California Press, Berkeley. 594 pp.
Historical records reviewed, no recent condor reports from area.

Grinnell, J., and A. H. Miller. 1944. The distribution of the birds of California. Pac. Coast Avifauna 27. 608 pp.
Distribution summary.

Grinnell, J., and H. S. Swarth. 1913. An account of the birds and mammals of the San Jacinto area of southern California. Univ. Calif. Publ. Zool. 10(10):197-406.
Condor former resident, no recent records.

Grinnell, J., and M. W. Wythe. 1927. Directory of the bird-life of the San Francisco Bay region. Pac. Coast Avifauna 18. 160 pp.
Summary of condor records; none since 1904.

Groner, D. E. 1956. [Cooper Ornithological Society meeting notes.] Condor 58(1):80.
Five condors seen near Fillmore, Ventura County, 16 October 1955.

Groner, D. E. 1958. [Cooper Ornithological Society meeting notes.] Condor 60(2):143.
At least 17 (possibly 25-30) condors at Mt. Pinos, Ventura County, 24 August 1957.

Gurney, J. H. 1894. Catalogue of the birds of prey with the number of specimens in Norwich Museum. London. 56 pp.
Museum had four skins, one skeleton, one egg on condor. "Lord Walsingham has shot vultures a good bit north of Mendocino (northern California), probably the rare *Pseudogryphus (Gymnogyps) californianus.*"

Hall, F. W. 1933a. Studies in the history of ornithology in the State of Washington (1792-1932) with special reference to the discovery of new species. Part II, Lewis and Clark. Murrelet 14(3):55-70.
Summarizes condor sightings by Lewis and Clark, Columbia River area, 1806.

Hall, F. W. 1933b. Studies in the history of ornithology in the State of Washington. Part III, David Douglas, Murrelet 15(1):3-19.
Summarizes David Douglas condor records.

Hamilton, A. 1952. Can the condor come back? Sci. Dig. 31(2):27-31.
Popular summary, past and present.

Harris, H. 1928. Robert Ridgway. Condor 30(1):4-118.
Dr. Langley condor flight computations discussed.

Harris, H. 1941. The annals of *Gymnogyps* to 1900. Condor 43(1):3-55.
Excellent summary of early written records of condors.

Harrison, G. 1967. The valley of the condors. Natl. Wildl. 5(6):4-9.
Popular account of trip to Sespe Condor Sanctuary.

Heald, W. F. 1960. Last stand of the California condor. Frontiers 25(2):105-106, 128.
Popular summary.

Heermann, A. L. 1859. Report of explorations and surveys for a railroad route from the Mississippi River to the Pacific Ocean, 1853-56. Vol. 10, Part 4, pages 29-80 *in* Report upon the birds collected on the survey. Beverly Tucker, Washington.
Records for Tejon Valley, Kern County, 1853; two nests presumably seen in the Sierra Nevada, one in San Diego County.

Heizer, R. F., and G. W. Hewes. 1940. Animal ceremonialism in central California in the light of archeology. Am. Anthropol., New Ser. 42(4):587-603.
Bones and feet of condors and other raptors found in Indian burial sites, apparently part of regalia rather than actual burial of birds.

Henshaw, H. W. 1875. Report upon the ornithological collections made in portions of Nevada, Utah, California, Colorado and New Mexico during the years 1871, 1872, 1873 and 1874. Vol. V., Chapter III, pages 133-508 *in* U.S. Geographical Survey west of the 100th Meridian. U.S. Government Printing Office, Washington, D.C.
  One condor seen feeding on a dead horse with turkey vultures, Beaver, Utah, 25 November 1872.

Henshaw, H. W. 1876. Report on the ornithology of the portions of California visited during the field season of 1875. Pages 224-278 *in* G. M. Wheeler, Annual report upon the geographical survey west of the 100th Meridian in California, Nevada, Utah, Colorado, Wyoming, New Mexico, Arizona and Montana. U.S. Government Printing Office, Washington, D.C.
  Few condors seen; "it seems highly probable that great numbers of these birds" have died from eating strychnine-poisoned carcasses (but no details given).

Henshaw, H. W. 1920. Autobiographical notes. Condor 22(1):3-10.
  Four condors seen at Mission San Antonio, Monterey County, 27 September 1884; hunter later collected three specimens for Henshaw.

Hess, C. N. 1930. King condor. Touring Topics 22(8):18-21, 56.
  Comprehensive popular article.

Hess, C. N. 1957. Sky sovereign. Westways 49(3):20-21.
  Popular account.

Hill, B. M., and I. L. Wiggins. 1948. Ornithological notes from lower California. Condor 50(4):155-161.
  Summary of earlier sightings, no condors since 1935.

Hill, N. P. 1944. Sexual dimorphism in the Falconiformes. Auk 61(2):228-234.
  Wing, tail, tarsus, and culmen measurements show male and female condors about same size.

Hilton, J. R. 1971. What fate for *Gymnogyps*? Calif. Condor (Society for the Preservation of Birds of Prey) 6(2):1-5.
  Popular summary of recent research and management.

Hilton, J. R. 1976. California condor: captive breeding in its future? Raptor Rep. 4(3):15.
  Pros and cons of captive propagation discussed.

Hoffman, W. H. 1895. Notes on California condors. Avifauna 1(2):17-19.
  Condor egg collection records.

Hoffmann, R. 1930. California condor. Gull 12(10):6.
  Recent (no date) sighting of 10 condors (8 adults, 2 immatures) in Sisquoc Falls Area, Santa Barbara County.

Holland, H. 1945. America's largest flyer. Fauna 7(3):86-89.
  General account of history and current status.

Holmes, F. H. 1897. A pet condor. Nidiologist 4(6):58-59.
Description and photos of captive immature "Ben Butler."

Hovland, C., and D. Hovland. 1972. America's endangered wildlife. Tower Publications, New York. 182 pp.
Pages 37-42, popular account, some inaccuracies.

Howard, H. 1929. The avifauna of Emeryville shellmound. Univ. Calif. Publ. Zool. 32(2):301-394.
Bones of one condor found.

Howard, H. 1930. A census of the Pleistocene birds of Rancho La Brea from the collections of the Los Angeles Museum. Condor 32(2):81-89.
Pleistocene *Gymnogyps* abundant in the fossil record.

Howard, H. 1938. [Cooper Ornithological Society meeting notes.] Condor 40(3):132.
Hearsay report of condor found dead after feeding on deer carcass; another condor caught in an animal trap.

Howard, H. 1947. A preliminary survey of trends in avian evolution from Pleistocene to recent times. Condor 49(1):10-13.
All Pleistocene condors now considered *G. amplus.*

Howard, H. 1952. The prehistoric avifauna of Smith Creek Cave, Nevada, with a description of a new gigantic raptor. Bull. South. Calif. Acad. Sci. 51(2):50-54.
Five bone fragments tentatively classified as *Gymnogyps.*

Howard, H. 1962a. Bird remains from a prehistoric cave deposit in Grant County, New Mexico. Condor 64(3):241-242.
At least eight individual condors represented, including three very young birds.

Howard, H. 1962b. A comparison of avian assemblages from individual pits at Rancho La Brea, California. Los Ang. Cty. Mus. Contrib. Sci. 58. 24 pp.
Two hundred fifteen *Gymnogyps amplus* specimens, apparently more in older pits than in more recent deposits.

Howard, H. 1971. Quaternary avian remains from Dark Canyon Cave, New Mexico. Condor 73(2):237-240.
Seventeen bones of *Gymnogyps amplus* found; previous identification of condor bones in Shelter Cave (Howard and Miller 1933) in error, bones reassigned to *Breagyps.*

Howard, H. 1974. Postcranial elements of the extinct condor *Breagyps clarki* (Miller). Los Ang. Nat. Hist. Mus., Contrib. Sci. 256:1-24.
Detailed comparison of bones with those of *Gymnogyps* and *Vultur.*

Howard, H., and A. H. Miller. 1933. Bird remains from cave deposits in New Mexico. Condor 35(1):15-18.
Condor bones found in two caves.

Howard, H., and A. H. Miller. 1939. The avifauna associated with human remains at Rancho La Brea, California. Carnegie Inst. Publ. 514:39-48.
Only one condor specimen in pit containing human remains.

Howard, J. and M. Howard. 1967. Condor. Better Camping 8(9):32-35.
Where and how to observe condors.

Howland, S. 1882. Golden eagle's eggs. Ornithol. Oologist 7(17):131.
Notes that J. G. Cooper has condor egg in possession.

Hubbard, F. 1969. 130 man survey team reports 52 condors. Outdoor Calif. 30(1):4-5.
1968 cooperative survey results.

Hubbard, F. 1972. California's condor — winning or losing? Outdoor Calif. 33(6):1.
1972 cooperative survey.

Huey, L. M. 1926. Notes from northwestern Lower California, with the description of an apparently new race of the screech owl. Auk 43(3):347-362.
One condor in Sierra San Pedro Martir, 12 June 1923; one condor in Sierra Juarez, 21 July 1924.

Huey, L. M. 1938. Frank Stephens, pioneer. Condor 40(3):101-110.
November 1908, one condor seen on Mexican border near Pacific Ocean.

Hunter, J. S. 1904. Records from the vicinity of Watsonville, California. Condor 6(1):24-25.
Summer 1903, condors seen several times.

Ingersoll, A. M. 1919. Albert Mills Ingersoll — an autobiography. Condor 21(2):53-57.
Brief mention of condor egg in his possession.

James, G. W. 1906. The wonders of the Colorado Desert. Little, Brown and Co., Boston. 547 pp.
Reports a condor killed, details not clear.

Jenkins, H. O. 1906. A list of birds collected between Monterey and San Simeon in the Coast Range of California. Condor 8(5):122-130.
Eight to ten condors roosting in redwood grove, Villa Creek, Monterey County, 18 July 1905.

Jewett, S. C., W. P. Taylor, W. T. Shaw, and J. W. Aldrich. 1953. Birds of Washington State. University Washington Press, Seattle. 767 pp.
Summarizes Washington records; last record apparently 30 September 1897, one bird near Coulee City.

Johnson, H. T. 1945. California condors in San Luis Obispo County, California. Condor 47(1):38.
Twenty condors feeding on animal carcass, Cholame Flats, 14 June 1944.

Jordan, D. S. 1922. The days of a man. Vol. I. World Book Co., Yonkers on Hudson. 709 pp.
Condors seen and reportedly nesting, 1904-1908, Pinnacles area, San Benito County.

Josephy, A. M. Jr. 1951. Condors don't pay taxes. Blue Book, December: 52-55.
Popular account of establishing Sespe Condor Sanctuary.

Keast, D. N. 1965. The noise environment of the California condor. Bolt, Beranek and Newman, Inc., Los Angeles. 29 pp.
Evaluates noise levels in Sespe Condor Sanctuary in relation to proposed Sespe Water Project.

Kellogg, F. L. 1910. Mallophagan parasites from the California condor. Science 31(784):33-34.
   Two species, *Menopon* and *Lipeurus,* removed from one condor specimen.

Kelly, A. 1906. How the condor seeks its food. Outing 47(6):782.
   A number of condors (unspecified, but apparently quite a few) attracted to a cow carcass on Tejon Ranch, Kern County.

Kermode, F. 1904. Catalogue of British Columbia birds. Victoria, B.C. 69 pp.
   Condor records summarized; concludes it is an accidental visitant.

Kessler, J. 1941. The big three. Cassinia 31:25-33.
   1937, two condors seen in Sespe Canyon, Ventura County.

Kofoid, C. A. 1923. An early account of the California condor. Condor 25(1):29-30.
   Adolphe Boucard description of condors on whale, San Francisco, 1851 or 1852.

Koford, C. B. 1953a. [Photograph of nestling condor.] Condor 55(3):150.

Koford, C. B. 1953b. The California condor. Natl. Audubon Soc. Res. Rep. 4. 154 pp.
   Monographic study of condors, particularly nesting activity.

Kohls, G. M., and H. Hoogstraal. 1960. Observations on the subgenus *Argas* (Ixodoidea, Argasidae, *Argas*). 2 *A. Cooleyi,* new species, from western North American birds. Annals Entomol. Soc. Am. 53(5):625-631.
   Tick recorded three times in vicinity of condor nest.

Kroeber, A. L. 1906-07. Indian myths of south central California. Univ. Calif. Publ. Am. Archeol. Ethnol. 4(4):167-250.
   Condor (called "wech") portrayed as bad influence in three Yokut myths.

Kroeber, A. L. 1908. A mission record of the California Indians. Univ. Calif. Publ. Am. Archeol. Ethnol. 8(1):1-127.
   Luiseno Indian name for condor is "Yungavaiwot"; condor not as important in ceremonies as is eagle.

Kroeber, A. L. 1925. Handbook of the Indians of California. Smithson. Inst. Bur. Am. Ethnol. Bull., 78. 995 pp.
   Condor described in legends and ceremonies of Indian tribes throughout California.

Kroeber, A. L. 1929. The Valley Nisenan. Univ. Calif. Publ. Am. Archeol. Ethnol. 24(4):253-290.
   Sacramento Valley Indians included condor (mo'lok') in myth about origin of fire.

Kushlan, J. A. 1973. Spread-wing posturing in cathartid vultures. Auk 90(4):889-890.
   Comparative behavior of vultures.

Larson, G. C. 1975. Westerlies: Sanctuary. Flying 96(5):80-81.
   Popular account of aircraft restrictions in condor nesting areas.

Law, L. B. 1934a. [Meeting notes, Cooper Ornithological Club.] Condor 36(1):48.
   S. Peyton reports two probable nestlings in Sespe Area.

Law, L. B. 1934b. [Meeting notes, Cooper Ornithological Club.] Condor 36(4):184.
Six condors seen, Sespe Canyon, 22 April 1934.

Law, L. B. 1935. [Meeting notes, Cooper Ornithological Club.] Condor 37(4):221.
Clam shells in 1934 condor nest; two condors seen, Gaviota Pass, Santa Barbara County.

Lawrence, R. E. 1893. *Pseudogryphus californianus.* Auk 10(3):300-301.
Data on three condor specimens.

Lawrence, R. E. 1894. The California vulture in the San Gabriel Range, California. Auk 11(1):76-77.
Condor shot at, but apparently not killed.

Laycock, G. 1968. The rancher and the condors. Farm Q. 23(3):74-75,86,90,92.
Popular status report.

Leach, F. A. 1929. A turkey buzzard roost. Condor 31(1):21-23.
Napa County, California: condors frequently seen 1857-1860, seldom seen after 1860.

Levy, C. 1965. The California condor. Calif. Monthly 75(3):44-45.
Popular summary of Miller et al. 1965.

Ligon, J. D. 1967. Relationship of the Cathartid vultures. Occas. Pap. Mus. Zool., Univ. Mich. 651:1-26.
Concludes that Cathartidae "are not at all closely related to the remainder of the Falconiformes, that they share a great many features with the storks, Cinconiidae."

Linsdale, J. M. 1936. The birds of Nevada. Pac. Coast Avifauna 23. 145 pp.
One post-Pleistocene record for the State.

Linsdale, J. M. 1951. A list of the birds of Nevada. Condor 53(5):228-249.
One post-Pleistocene record for the State.

Linton, C. B. 1908. Notes from Buena Vista Lake, May 20 to June 16, 1907. Condor 10(5):196-198.
"Reported breeding in mountains near lake."

Locke, L. N., G. E. Bagley, D. N. Frickie, and L. T. Young. 1969. Lead poisoning and aspergillosis in an Andean condor. J. Am. Vet. Med. Assoc. 155(7):1052-1056.
Lead shot ingested with food; suggest California condor may be susceptible to same.

Loeb, E. M. 1926. Pomo folkways. Univ. Calif. Publ. Am. Archeol. Ethnol. 19(2):149-404.
Pages 384-385, Pomo condor dance described.

Lofberg, L. M. 1936. Twenty condors dine together. Condor 38(4):177.
Twenty condors on sheep carcass east of Bakersfield, Kern County, 25 April 1936; winter 1936, "good authority" reports six condors in Breckenridge Mountain area, Kern County.

Lovejoy, T. 1976. We must decide which species will go forever. Smithsonian 7(4):52-59.
Using a trip to see condors as a springboard, discusses the problems of impending extinctions and concludes (unhappily) that we may have to set up a system of deciding what to save and what not to save.

Lucas, F. A. 1891. Animals recently extinct or threatened with extermination, as represented in the collections of the United States National Museum. Pages 609-649 in Annual Report of the U.S. National Museum, 1889.
Doubts that killing condors for their quills was an important mortality factor.

Lume, C. R. 1938. Stalking America's mightiest bird. Travel Mag. 70(3):30-31, 52-53.
Dramatic and exaggerated story of collecting a condor egg in Baja California.

Lyon, M. W., Jr. 1918. [Report of the Secretary. Biological Society of Washington, 20 October 1917.] J. Wash. Acad. Sci. 8(1):25-28.
Fall 1879, sight record of two condors feeding on sheep carcass near Boise, Idaho.

MacDonald, R. 1964. A death road for the condor. Sports Illus. 20(14):86-89.
Sierra Madre Ridge Road proposal, Santa Barbara County.

Macoun, J., and J. M. Macoun. 1909. Catalogue of Canadian birds. Government Printing Office, Ottawa. 761 pp.
Several pre-1893 British Columbia records; refutes Alberta sighting (Fannin 1897).

Mailliard, J., and J. W. Mailliard. 1901. Birds recorded at Paicines, San Benito Co., California. Condor 3(5):120-127.
Formerly abundant, now rarely seen.

Mallette, R. D. 1970. Operational management plan for California condor. California Department of Fish and Game, Sacramento. 58 pp.
Management and research guidelines.

Mallette, R. D. 1971. Results of California condor baiting effort, 1967-1969. Calif. Dep. Fish Game, Wildl. Manage. Branch Adm. Rep. 71-76. 7 pp.
Short-term baiting programs have limited effectiveness.

Mallette, R. D., and J. C. Borneman. 1966. First cooperative survey of the California condor. Calif. Fish Game 52(3):185-203.
Thirty-eight condors estimated seen.

Mallette, R. D., J. C. Borneman, F. C. Sibley, and R. S. Dalen. 1967. Second cooperative survey of the California condor. Calif. Fish Game 53(3):132-145.

Mallette, R. D., F. C. Sibley, W. D. Carrier, and J. C. Borneman. 1970. California condor surveys, 1969. Calif. Fish Game 56(3):199-202.
Fifty-three birds estimated seen.

Mallette, R. D., and F. C. Sibley. 1971. California condor surveys, 1965-1969. Biol. Conserv. 3(2):143-145.
Summary of techniques and results.

Mallette, R. D., S. R. Wilbur, W. D. Carrier, and J. C. Borneman. 1972. California condor survey, 1970. Calif. Fish Game 58(1):67-68.
Twenty-eight condors estimated seen.

Mallette, R. D., S. R. Wilbur, W. D. Carrier, and J. C. Borneman. 1973. California condor survey, 1972. Calif. Fish Game 59(4):317-318.
Thirty-six condors estimated seen.

Mariana, N., Jr. 1968. Valley of the condors. Ranger Rick's Nat. Mag. 2(2):15-19.
Children's account of condor watching trip.

May, J. 1972. Giant condor of California. Creative Educational Society, Inc., Mankato. 37 pp.
Children's account, well done.

May, R. H. 1941. A condor in the San Jacinto Mountains, California. Condor 43(4):199.
Possible sighting of a condor, 15 January 1941.

McClure, H. E. 1950. Condors. News from the bird-banders 25(1):14.
March 1949, up to 25 condors seen regularly east of Bakersfield, Kern County, California.

McCoy, J. J. 1963. The fossil avifauna of Itchtucknee River, Florida. Auk 80(3):335-351.
One bone of *Gymnogyps amplus.*

McGregor, R. C. 1899. Some summer birds of Palomar Mountains, from the notes of J. Maurice Hatch. Condor 1(4):67-68.
June 1897, San Diego County, four condors seen, reputedly breeding in area.

McGregor, R. C. 1901. A list of the land birds of Santa Cruz County, California. Pac. Coast Avifauna 2. 22 pp.
Apparently common in county, breeding in mountains north of Santa Cruz prior to 1900.

McLain, R. B. 1898. The California vulture in Santa Barbara County, California. Auk 15(2):185.
February 1898, condor collected at Lompoc.

McMillan, I. 1953. Condors, politics and game management. Central California Sportsman, reprint from December issue. 3 pp.
San Diego Zoo condor trapping controversy.

McMillan, I. 1965a. An objection to feeding California condors. Defenders of Wildl. News 40(2):45-46.
Extra food not needed, unnatural to provide it.

McMillan, I. 1965b. Shall we save the condor or build another dam? Defenders Wildl. News 40(4):39-40.
Against Sespe Water Project.

McMillan, I. 1966. Poisoned condors. Defenders Wildl. News 41(2):115-116.
Condors possibly poisoned by animal-control projects.

McMillan, I. 1967. Game management vs. condor preservation. Defenders Wildl. News 42(4):365-369.
Criticism of current condor management.

McMillan, I. 1968. Man and the California condor. Dutton and Co., New York. 191 pp.
Popular treatment of condor history and management.

McMillan, I. 1970. Botching the condor program. Defenders Wildl. News 45(1):95-98.
Criticism of recent research and management.

McMillan, I. 1971. The 1971 condor survey — a return to soundness. Defenders Wildl. News 46(4):386.
Comments on annual survey.

McMillan, I. 1975. Man and the condor. West. Tanager 42(2):1-2.
General comments on the condor and its preservation.

Meadows, C. 1933. California condor in San Diego County. Condor 35(6):234.
Two condors seen near Mt. Palomar, 3 August 1933.

Merriam, C. H. 1910. The dawn of the world. Arthur Clark Co., Cleveland. 273 pp.
Condor an important mythological character for the California Miwok Indians.

Mertz, D. B. 1971. The mathematical demography of the California condor population. Am. Nat. 105(945):437-453.
Mathematic analysis of condor population.

Mery, S. 1965. He was there! Scissortail (Okla. Ornithol. Soc.) 15(3):57-58.
Witness to accidental death of immature condor.

Millard, R. 1958. Feathered giant of the skies. Coronet 43(5):144-146.
San Diego Zoo condor trapping attempt.

Miller, A. H. 1937. Biotic associations and life-zones in relation to Pleisto-cene birds of California. Condor 39(6):248-252.
Vegetation and climatic change.

Miller, A. H. 1942. A California condor bone from the coast of southern Oregon. Murrelet 23(3):77.
Found with pre-caucasian Indian artifacts.

Miller, A. H. 1951. [Notes and news section.] Condor 53(2):103.
Restrictions on oil and gas development in Sespe area.

Miller, A. H. 1953a. More trouble for the California condor. Condor 55(1):47-48.
San Diego Zoo permit to trap condors.

Miller, A. H. 1953b. The case against trapping California condors. Audubon Mag. 55(6):261-262.
Propagation and release to wild not feasible; trapping might disrupt breeding pairs; condor in a cage is not a real condor.

Miller, A. H., and H. I. Fisher. 1938. The pterylosis of the California condor. Condor 40(6):248-256.
Old condor skin taken apart to study feather placement.

Miller, A. H., I. McMillan, and E. McMillan. 1964. The current status and welfare of the California condor. Sierra Club Bull. 49(9):13-16.
Summary of Miller et al. 1965a.

Miller, A. H., I. McMillan, and E. McMillan. 1965a. The current status and welfare of the California condor. Natl. Audubon Soc. Res. Rep. 6. 61 pp.
Evaluation of changes in population since Koford 1953b.

Miller, A. H., I. McMillan, and E. McMillan. 1965b. Hope for the California condor. Audubon Mag. 67(1):38-41.
Summary of Miller et al. 1965a.

Miller, L. H. 1910. The condor-like vultures of Rancho La Brea. Univ. Calif. Publ., Bull. Dep. Geol. 6(1):1-19.
Gymnogyps and others in tar pits.

Miller, L. H. 1911. Avifauna of the Pleistocene cave deposits of California. Univ. Calif., Bull. Dep. Geol. 6(16):385-400.
Condor remains in Shasta County.

Miller, L. H. 1912. Contribution to avian paleontology from the Pacific coast of North America. Univ. Calif., Bull. Dep. Geol. 7(5):61-115.
Discussion of causes of extinction, summary of fossil record.

Miller, L. H. 1925. The birds of Rancho La Brea. Carnegie Inst. Publ. 349:63-106.
Summary of fossil record.

Miller, L. H. 1927. Pleistocene fauna and flora. Bird remains. Science 66(1702): 155-156.
Condor from Carpinteria, Santa Barbara County, tarpits.

Miller, L. H. 1931. The California condor in Nevada. Condor 33(1):32.
One bone found in cave near Las Vegas.

Miller, L. H. 1937. Feather studies of the California condor. Condor 39(4):160-162.
Feather molt determined from specimen.

Miller, L. H. 1942. Succession in the cathartine dynasty. Condor 44(5):212-213.
Concludes condor is a "senile" species.

Miller, L. H. 1943. The Pleistocene birds of San Josecito Cavern, Mexico. Univ. Calif. Publ. Zool. 47(5):143-168.
Remains of about three individual condors.

Miller, L. H. 1957. Bird remains from an Oregon Indian midden. Condor 59(1):59-63.
Many bones from midden at The Dalles, Oregon.

Miller, L. H. 1960a. Condor remains from Rampart Cave, Arizona. Condor 62(1):70; 62(4):298.
Included are bones of a nestling bird.

Miller, L. H. 1960b. Condors of Lake Mead. Natl. Parks Mag. 34(156):8-9.
Rampart Cave bones.

Miller, L. H. 1960c. On the history of the Cathartidae in North America. Novedades Columbianus 1(5):232-235.
General summary.

Miller, L. H. 1968. In search of the California condor. West. Tanager 34(7):57-59, 64-65.
Field notes 1910, Los Angeles and Ventura counties.

Miller, L. H., and I. DeMay. 1942. The fossil birds of California. Univ. Calif. Publ. Zool. 47(4):47-142.
First record of condor bones at McKittrick, Kern County, tarpits.

Millikan, C. 1900. Capture of a condor in El Dorado Co., Cal. in 1854. Condor 2(1):12-13.
Autumn 1854, condor captured, eventually escaped.

Morcom, G. F. 1887. Notes on the birds of southern California and southwestern Arizona. Ridgway Ornithol. Club Bull. 2:36-57.
Frank Stephens notes on condors in San Bernardino County, summer 1886.

Morse, G. 1965. There soars the condor. Am. For. 71(2):22-24, 63.
Condor vs. Sierra Madre Ridge Road proposal.

Murphy, R. C. 1953. [Review of Koford 1953.] Audubon Mag. 55(5):232-233.
Notes "the inescapable fact that no one can give a categorical answer to the question (how can we save the condor)."

Nelson, E. W. 1921. Lower California resources. Memoirs Natl. Acad. Sci. 16(1):1-194.
Two condors collected in 1905; condor said to nest in Santa Rosa Canyon, Sierra San Pedro Martir (not confirmed).

Netboy, A. 1976. Thunderbird. Am. For. 83(12):8-10.
General summary of history and status.

Newberry, J. S. 1857. Report of explorations and surveys to ascertain the most practicable and economical route for a railroad from the Mississippi River to the Pacific Ocean. Vol. 6, Part 2, pages 73-110 in Report upon the zoology of the route. Beverly Tucker, Washington D.C.
Seen "every day" in Sacramento Valley, "very few" in Klamath Basin, 1854.

Nice, M. N. 1954. Problems of incubation periods in North American birds. Condor 56(4):173-197.
Notes that condor incubation period has been erroneously reported as 29-31 days.

Norris, J. P., Jr. 1926. A catalogue of sets of Accipitres' eggs in the collection of Joseph Parker Norris, Jr. Oologist's Rec. 6(2):25-41.
One condor egg collected 22 April 1900, Monterey County.

North, A. W. 1910. Camp and camino in Lower California. Baker and Taylor Co., New York. 346 pp.
January 1906, one condor seen, Sierra San Pedro Martir.

Orr, P. C. 1968. Prehistory of Santa Rosa Island. Santa Barbara Museum of Natural History. 253 pp.
Condor bones from Pleistocene.

Orr, R. T. 1966. Will the condor survive? Pac. Discovery 19(6):20-21.
Popular account.

Parker, H. 1965. The early Indians of Temecula. Paisano Press Inc., Balboa Island. 34 pp.
San Diego Indians may sometimes have substituted condor for eagle in eagle-killing ceremonies.

Parmalee, P. W. 1969. California condor and other birds from Stanton Cave, Arizona. J. Ariz. Acad. Sci. 5(4):204-206.
At least three individuals represented by bones.

Peale, T. R. 1957. Diary of Titian Ramsay Peale. Dawson's Book Store, Los Angeles. 85 pp.
Condor seen in Umpqua River area, Oregon, 24 September 1841; several condors near Mt. Shasta, California, 5 October 1841; "numbers of condors" seen in northern Sacramento Valley, California, 3 October 1841.

Peck, G. D. 1904. The California vulture in Douglas County, Oregon. Oologist 21(4):55.
June 1903, several condors seen.

Pemberton, J. R. 1910. Some bird notes from Ventura County, California. Condor 12(1):18-19.
June-July 1909, several sightings of one to three condors.

Pemberton, J. R., and H. W. Carriger. 1915. A partial list of the summer resident land birds of Monterey County, California. Condor 17(5):189-201.
One condor seen, other reported, 27 May 1909.

Pequegnat, W. E. 1945. A report upon the biota of the Santa Ana Mountains. J. Entomol. Zool. (Pomona College) 37(2):25-41.
Several records of one to two condors, 1937-1940.

Peterson, R. T. 1968. Vulture vigil on four continents. Audubon Mag. 70(6):82-97.
Condors in Sespe Condor Sanctuary area.

Peterson, R. T., and J. Fisher. 1955. Wild America. Houghton Mifflin Co., Boston. 434 pp.
Popular account of condor watching in Sespe area.

Peyton, S. B. 1932. Visiting the condor country. Oologist 49(2):23-24.
Five condors (two adults, three immatures) seen in Sespe Creek area, 23 March 1929.

Peyton, S. B. 1936. [Cooper Ornithological Club meeting notes.] Condor 38(5):223.
Condor reported captured at Tejon Ranch, later escaped.

Peyton, S. B. 1937. [Cooper Ornithological Club meeting notes.] Condor 39(2):95.
December 1936, dead condor found in Squaw Flat area, Ventura County; two others reported killed by hail (see Rett 1938).

Phillips, A., J. Marshall, and G. Monson. 1964. The birds of Arizona. University of Arizona Press, Tucson. 220 pp.
Summary of Arizona records; probable last date 1924.

Phillips, J. C. 1926. An attempt to list the extinct and vanishing birds of the Western Hemisphere, with some notes on recent status, location of specimens, etc. Int. Ornithol. Congr. 6:503-534.
J. Grinnell estimated 150 condors.

Porter, R., and C. Walker. 1969. New World vultures. Birds of the World 2(1):337-349.
General life history.

Poulsen, H. 1963. On the behavior of the South American condor (*Vultur gryphus* L.). Z. Tierpsychol. 20(4):468-473.
Compares behavior of the two species of condor.

Preston, J. 1908. An egg of the California vulture compared with those of other vultures. Oologist 25(4):57-58.
Egg described, no specimen details.

Pryor, A. 1965. The big battle over 39 birds. Calif. Farmer 223(6):20.
Arguments in favor of the Sespe Water Project.

Putnam, R. 1928. The letters of Roselle Putnam. Oreg. Hist. Q. 29(3):242-264.
Umpqua River, Oregon, record of a dead condor, 1852.

Pycraft, W. P. 1902. Contributions to the osteology of birds. Part 5, Falconiformes. Proc. Zool. Soc. London 1:277-320.
Condor compared with other species.

Ray, M. S. 1906. A-birding in an auto. Auk 23(4):400-418.
June 1905, single condors seen in Los Angeles and Santa Barbara counties.

Redington, A. P. 1899. Taking a condor's egg. Bull. Cooper Ornithol. Club 1(4):75.
Egg taken in Santa Ynez Mountains, Santa Barbara County, 17 April 1899; young condor allegedly shot in same area.

Redington, P. G. 1920. A California condor seen near head of Deer Creek. California Fish Game 6(3):133.
Condor landed in redwood tree, Tulare County, 11 May 1920.

Reed, C. A. 1965. North American birds eggs (1904 edition reprinted). Dover Publications, New York. 372 pp.
Description of bird and egg.

Reed, G. W., and R. Gaines, eds. 1949. The journals, drawings and other papers of J. Goldsborough Bruff, April 2, 1849-July 20, 1851. Columbia Univ. Press, New York. 794 pp.
One condor shot, Plumas or Tehama county, California, 20 October 1849; others seen in 1850.

Rehfus, R. 1968. California condor (*Gymnogyps californianus*), the literature since 1900. U.S. Dep. Inter. Libr. Bibliography 7A. 16 pp.
Listing of less obscure references.

Reid, H. A. 1895. History of Pasadena. Pasadena History Co., Pasadena. 675 pp.
November 1878, condor killed near Pasadena; specimen not saved.

Rett, E. Z. 1938. Hailstorm fatal to California condors. Condor 40(5):225.
October 1936, two condors in Santa Barbara County presumably killed by hailstones.

Rett, E. Z. 1946. Record of another condor death. Condor 48(4):182.
May 1945, eastern San Luis Obispo County, death caused by osteomyolitis?

Rhoads, S. N. 1892. The birds of southeastern Texas and southern Arizona observed during May, June and July 1891. Proc. Acad. Nat. Sci. Phila. 44:98-126.
Possible condor shot in central Arizona.

Rhoads, S. N. 1893. The birds observed in British Columbia and Washington during spring and summer 1892. Proc. Acad. Nat. Sci. Phila. 45:21-65.
Condor "used to be common" in British Columbia.

Richmond, C. W. 1901. On the generic name of the California condor. Condor 3(2):49.
Gymnogyps, name assigned in 1842; takes precedence over later terminology.

Ridgway, R. 1880. Notes on the American vultures (Sarcorhamphidae), with special reference to their generic nomenclature. Bull. Nuttall Ornithol. Club 5(2):77-84.
General comments and specimen measurements.

Ridgway, R. 1885. Remarks on the California vulture (*Pseudogryphus californianus*). Auk 2(2):167-169.
Specimen records and measurements.

Rising, H. 1899. Capture of a California condor. Condor 1(2):25-26.
Adult condor killed, nestling captured and raised as pet, Santa Monica Mountains, Los Angeles County, 25 August 1898.

Robertson, J. M. 1931. [Meeting notes, Cooper Ornithological Club.] Condor 33(5):228.
Twelve condors seen in southeastern Ventura County.

Robinson, C. S. 1940. Notes on the California condor, collected on Los Padres National Forest, California. U.S. Forest Service, Santa Barbara. 21 pp.
One of the most important summaries of information on the condor.

Roof, J. 1969. The disappearing California condor. Desert Mag. 32(3):16-19.
Popular status report.

Ross, A. 1956. The fur hunters of the far west. University of Oklahoma Press, Norman. 304 pp.
Page 137, probable record of condors in eastern Washington or Oregon in the fall of 1818.

St. John, R. 1931. Condors on the Santa Barbara National Forest. California Fish Game 17(1):88-89.
"Often seen," Santa Ynez and San Rafael mountains.

Sani, M. 1975. County role crucial to condors. Visalia (California) Times-Delta, 22 September 1975: 1, 8A.
Discusses importance of Tulare County as condor feeding area.

Schaeffer, C. E. 1951. Was the California condor known to the Blackfoot Indians? J. Wash. Acad. Sci. 41(6):181-191.
Indians of Montana and southern Canada report occasional visits by a very large, bald-headed bird.

Sclater, P. L. 1866. Living California vulture received in London. Proc. Zool. Soc. London 13:366.
Received from Dr. C. A. Canfield of Monterey, California.

Scott, C. D. 1936a. Are condors extinct in Lower California? Condor 38(1):41-42.
Concludes they are extinct or nearly so.

Scott, C. D. 1936b. Who killed the condor? Nat. Mag. 28(6):368-370.
Gunfire probably main factor in decline.

Scott, I. 1966. Interview with a dry condor. Scope 1(11):16.
Humorous look at the Sespe Dam controversy.

Scouler, J. 1905. Dr. John Scouler's journal of a voyage to northwest America. Oreg. Hist. Soc. Q. 6(2):276-287.
September 1825, Fort Vancouver, Washington, condor collected.

Seymour, G. 1971. California condor. Natl. Motorist 48(2):17-19.
Popular summary.

Sharp, C. S. 1907. The condor fifty years ago. Condor 9(5):160-161.
Egg presumably laid by captive condor in Paris — doubtful, as no live condors are known to have been in France.

Sharp, C. S. 1918. Concerning a condor. Oologist 35(1):8-11.
San Diego County, 1901, an immature condor shot.

Sharples, R. P. 1897. The taking of a California condor's egg. Osprey 2(2):21.
Egg taken, reportedly in Monterey County, 11 March 1897 (Willett 1933 says San Diego County).

Shaw, E. W. 1970. California condor. Library of Congress Legislative Reference Service SK-351, 70-127-EP. 10 pp.
General summary, considerable misinformation.

Sheldon, H. H. 1939. What price condor? Field and Stream 44(5):22-23, 61-62.
Popular anti-condor article, concludes that condor has outlived its usefulness.

Shields, A. M. 1895. Nesting of the California vulture. Nidiologist 2(11):148-150.
Condor egg collected, 25 April 1895, location uncertain.

Shufeldt, R. W. 1881. The claw on the index digit of the Cathartidae. Am. Nat. 15(11):906-908.
New World vultures have claw; Old World vultures do not.

Shufeldt, R. W. 1883. Osteology of the Cathartidae. Annu. Rep., U.S. Geol. Geograph. Surv. 12(1):727-786.
Detailed comparisons.

Sibley, C. G. 1952. The birds of the south San Francisco Bay region. 42 pp. [Copy at Oakland (California) Public Library.]
Summary of records; not uncommon prior to 1880, now possible rare vagrant.

Sibley, F. C. 1969. Effects of the Sespe Creek Project on the California condor. U.S. Fish and Wildlife Service, Laurel, Maryland. 19 pp.
Effects of noise and disturbances on condors.

Sibley, F. C. 1970. Annual nesting of the California condor. Paper presented at annual meeting, Cooper Ornithological Society, Fort Collins, Colorado, 20 June 1970. 3 pp.
One nest cliff fledged condors in four consecutive years.

Sibley, F. C., R. D. Mallette, J. C. Borneman, and R. S. Dalen. 1968. Third cooperative survey of the California condor. Calif. Fish Game 54(4):297-303.
Minimum of 46 condors estimated.

Sibley, F. C., R. D. Mallette, J. C. Borneman, and R. S. Dalen. 1969. California condor surveys, 1968. Calif. Fish Game 55(4):298-306.
Minimum of 52 condors estimated.

Siddon, D. 1967. Perched on the brink of oblivion. Los Angeles Times, West Magazine, 5 March:27-29.
Popular account of current situation.

Siebert, M. 1941. A week with the California condor. Field Ornithol. 3(1-2): 3-6.
March 1940, at least 10 condors seen in Sespe area.

Silverman, M. 1951. The fabulous condor's last stand. Saturday Evening Post 223(41):36, 148-150.
Establishing Sisquoc Condor Sanctuary, and later conservation efforts.

Simon, N., and P. Geroudet. 1970. Last survivors. World Publishing Co., New York. 275 pp.
Pages 57-61, summary of life history and conservation.

Skirm, J. 1884. List of birds of Santa Cruz, Cal. Ornithol. and Oologist 9(12):149-150.
Condors "common."

Smith, D. 1966. Condors and guns. Defenders Wildl. News 41(4):320-322.
Deer hunting seen as threat to condors.

Smith, D., and R. Easton. 1964. California condor, vanishing American. McNally and Loftin, Santa Barbara. 111 pp.
Popular life history and conservation.

Smith, D., and R. Easton. 1965a. The condor controversy: an on-the-spot report. Defenders Wildl. News 40(4):40-42.
Sespe Water Project vs. condors.

Smith, D., and R. Easton. 1965b. The condor controversy. Westways 57(7):20-21.
Sespe Water Project vs. condors.

Smith, D., and R. Easton. 1965c. The condor controversy. Anim. Life 40:22-23.
Sespe Water Project vs. condors.

Smith, F. J. 1916. Occurrence of the condor in Humboldt County. Condor 18(5):205.
Once "plentiful" in northwestern California.

Sparkman, P. S. 1908. The culture of the Luiseno Indians. Univ. Calif. Publ. Archeol. Ethnol. 8(4):187-234.
Condor feathers used for ceremonial dress, San Diego County.

Speer, L. 1971. Can this bird survive? Dodge News Mag. 36(2):3-5.
Popular account of conservation efforts.

Stager, K. 1964. The role of olfaction in food location by the turkey vulture (*Cathartes aura*). Los Ang. Cty. Mus. Contrib. Sci. 81:1-63.
"No evidence . . . that olfaction plays more than a minor role, if any, in food location by . . . *Gymnogyps*."

Stephens, F. 1895. Notes on the California vulture. Auk 12(1):81-82.
Kern County, 10 October 1894, 26 condors at a horse carcass.

Stephens, F. 1899. Lassoing a California vulture. Bull. Cooper Ornithol. Club 1(5):88.
San Diego County, 24 May 1899, one condor captured.

Stephens, F. 1919. An annotated list of the birds of San Diego County, California. Trans. San Diego Soc. Nat. Hist. 3(2):1-40.
Formerly common, once again increasing.

Stephenson, T. 1948. The shadows of Old Saddleback. Fine Arts Press, Orange, Calif. 207 pp.
Pages 127-132, condor presumably nesting in Santa Ana Mountains.

Stewart, G. W. 1908. The condor in the San Joaquin Valley. Condor 10(3):130.
"Formerly not uncommon," recent hearsay records.

Stillman, J. D. B. 1967. The gold rush letters. Lewis Osborne, Palo Alto. 75 pp.
Adult condor shot on Sacramento River in Colusa County, 19 September 1849.

Stone, W. 1905. On a collection of birds and mammals from the Colorado Delta, Lower California. Proc. Acad. Nat. Sci. Phila. 57:676-690.
One condor seen, 1905.

Storer, J. H. 1948. The flight of birds. Cranbrook Inst. Sci. Bull. 28. 94 pp.
Pages 44-45 and 64-71, aerodynamics of condor wing.

Streator, C. P. 1886. List of birds observed in the vicinity of Santa Barbara, Cal., during the year 1885. Ornithol. and Oologist 11(5):66-67.
Condor occasionally seen.

Streator, C. P. 1888. Notes on the California condor. Ornithol. and Oologist 13(2):30.
Suggests (no evidence) many condors killed by poisons.

Sumner, L. 1950. Condors observed from airplane. Condor 52(3):133.
Two condors observed, Los Angeles County.

Sumner, L., and J. S. Dixon. 1953. Birds and mammals of the Sierra Nevada. Univ. California Press, Berkeley. 484 pp.
Compilation of records in and near Sequoia National Park.

Sutter, J. 1972. Vanishing species. Buffalo (New York) Courier-Express, 19 March 1972, Magazine section:12-13.
General account of condor status.

Swann, H. K. 1924. Monograph of the birds of prey. Vol. 1, Part 1. Weldon and Wesley, London. 51 pp.
Describes condor egg from Baja California.

Swarth, H. S. 1914. A distributional list of the birds of Arizona. Pac. Coast Avifauna 10. 133 pp.
Considers all Arizona records doubtful.

Swarth, H. S. 1934. In memorium: George Frean Morcom, March 16, 1845-March 25, 1932. Condor 36(1):16-24.
Two condor eggs in Morcom collection.

Swift, L. W. 1945. Our national forests as a home for wildlife. Audubon Mag. 47(5):288-295.
Brief popular treatment of condor.

Taylor, A. S. 1855. Note on the great vulture of California. Zoologist 13:4632-4635.
One of earliest comprehensive accounts; much misinformation.

Taylor, A. S. 1859a. The egg and young of the California condor. Hutching's Calif. Mag. 3(12):537-540.
First published description of nest, egg and chick.

Taylor, A. S. 1859b. The great condor of California. Hutching's Calif. Mag. 3(12):540-543, 4(1):17-22, 4(2):61-64.
Basis of most early bird book accounts, although full of hearsay and obvious misinformation.

Taylor, B. 1949. Eldorado, or adventures in the path of empire. Alfred A. Knopf, New York. 375 pp.
September 1849, near Livermore (Alameda County), both buzzards and "mountain vultures" (condors?) seen.

Taylor, H. R. 1893. Killed with small shot. Nidiologist 1(1):6.
Condor killed in San Benito County.

Taylor, H. R. 1894. After condor's eggs. Nidiologist 1(6):109.
Unsuccessful egg hunt.

Taylor, H. R. 1895a. Habits of the California condor. Nidiologist 2(6):73-79.
Compilation of various observers' information.

Taylor, H. R. 1895b. Collecting a condor's egg. Nidiologist 2(7):88-89.
May 1889, condor egg from San Luis Obispo County.

Taylor, H. R. 1895c. [Open letter to W. F. Webb.] Nidiologist 2(7):100.
Webb's catalogue lists condor eggs at $25; Taylor offers him $250 for three or less!

Taylor, H. R. 1895d. [Editorial notes.] Nidiologist 2(9):130.
More on Webb's catalogue.

Taylor, H. R. 1895e. Wholesale frauds. Nidiologist 2(11):150.
Warns that some may try to sell swan's eggs for condor eggs.

Taylor, H. R. 1985f. On the eggs of the California vulture. Nidiologist 3(4-5):42.
Nine eggs described.

Taylor, H. R. 1898. Early nidification of California vulture. Osprey 3(2):29.
March 1898, two eggs collected.

Test, F. H. 1941. An afternoon with California condors. Indiana Audubon Year Book 19:24-28.
April 1940, 17 condors seen in mountains near Fillmore.

Todd, F. S. 1968. The thunderbird. Zoo View 3(4):3-5.
Popular account of captive condor, and of current management.

Todd, F. S. 1974. Maturation and behavior of the California condor at the Los Angeles Zoo. Int. Zoo Yearb. 14:145-147.
Behavior of a captive condor.

Todd, F. S. 1975. The tenacious thunderbirds. Wildlife 17(1):8-13.
Popular summary of status and management.

Todd, F. S., and N. B. Gale. 1970. Further notes on the California condor at Los Angeles Zoo. Int. Zoo Yearb. 10:15-17.
Plumage changes of captive immature condor.

Tolmie, W. F. 1963. William Fraser Tolmie, physician and fur trader. Mitchell Press Ltd., British Columbia. 413 pp.
Ft. McLoughlin, British Columbia, 24 November 1834, probable record of a condor.

Torrey, B. 1913. Field-days in California. Houghton Mifflin Co., Boston. 234 pp.
Pages 93-99, popular account of seeing a condor in Los Angeles County.

Townsend, C. H. 1887. Field-notes on the mammals, birds and reptiles of northern California. Proc. U.S. Natl. Mus. 10:159-241.
Once common in northern California, records given for Tehama County prior to 1884.

Townsend, J. K. 1848. Popular monograph on the accipitrine birds of N.A. — No. II, Californian vulture. Lit. Rec. and J. Linnean Assoc., Penn. Coll. 4(12):265-272.
Oregon, 1835, condors seen regularly; one killed.

Truslow, F. K. 1974. How I photographed America's largest bird. Natl. Wildl. 12(2):35-39.
Picture story.

Turner, A. W. 1973. Vultures. David McKay Co., Inc., New York. 95 pp.
Elementary coverage of life history of California condor and other vultures.

Tyler, J. G. 1913. Some birds of the Fresno district, California. Pac. Coast Avifauna 9. 114 pp.
Reported in 1900 and 1911.

U.S. Fish and Wildlife Service. 1969. A detailed report on the Sespe Creek Project. Portland, Oregon. 39 pp.
Probable effects on condor and other wildlife.

U.S. Fish and Wildlife Service. 1973. Threatened wildlife of the United States. Resour. Publ. 114. 289 pp.
Outline of life history and management.

U.S. National Park Service. 1974. Threatened wildlife of the Western Region. San Francisco. 68 pp.
Review of status within National Park System.

United Water Conservation District. 1965a. The California condor management and protection program. Santa Paula, California. 15 pp.
Alternatives to National Audubon Society program for condor protection, in relation to proposed Sespe Water Project.

United Water Conservation District. 1965b. Audubon Society vs. United Water, just who is fighting who for what? United Water News 6(1):2-3.
Sespe Water Project controversy.

Van Denburgh, J. 1898. Birds observed in central California in the summer of 1893. Proc. Acad. Nat. Sci. Phila. 50:206-218.
Owens Valley, 19 July 1893, one condor seen.

Van Denburgh, J. 1899. Notes on some birds of Santa Clara County, California. Proc. Am. Philos. Soc. 38(160):157-180.
Four condors near Los Gatos, no date given.

Vaughan, T. 1971. Russian museums: a unique trip by rail. West. Mus. Q. 7(3):1-7.
Leningrad museum has Indian capes made of condor feathers, obtained from Fort Ross, Sonoma County, California.

Verner, J. 1976. An appraisal of the continued involvement of Forest Service research in the California condor recovery program. U.S. Forest Service, Pacific Southwest Forest and Range Experiment Station, Berkeley. 28 pp.
Computer modeling of condor population, concludes that adult survival rate has been about 95%, and immature survival rate 85%. Recommendations for future research included in report.

Vincent, J. 1966. Red data book. Vol. 2 — Aves. Internation Union for Conservation of Nature and Natural Resources. Looseleaf, coded but unnumbered.
Outline of current status and management.

Wallace, W. J., and D. W. Lathrap. 1959. Ceremonial bird burials in San Francisco Bay shellmounds. Am. Antiq. 25(2):262-264.
Presence of entire condor skeleton suggests purposeful burial.

Watson, B. 1965. Conservation notes. West. Tanager 31(7):65, 68.
Plans to organize a "condor patrol" to help with law enforcement and education.

Webb, J. J. 1935. The condor and its nesting site. Gull 17(10):1-2.
"Nest" (more likely roost) seen in Sespe Creek area, 14 July 1935.

Webb, J. J. 1937. California condor and other birds of Sespe Canyon. Gull 19(8):1-3.
Eight condors seen, 3 May 1937.

Webb, J. J. 1939. Inquisitiveness of California condor, Pacific horned owl, and golden eagle. Gull 21(4):1.
Condors appear to intentionally approach people.

Westwood, R. W. 1953. Contents noted. Nat. Mag. 46(6):287.
Trapping proposal by San Diego Zoo.

Wetmore, A. 1931a. The California condor in New Mexico. Condor 33(2):76-77.
Two bones in cave deposits.

Wetmore, A. 1931b. The avifauna of the Pleistocene in Florida. Smithson. Misc. Coll. 85(2):1-41.
Condor bones found in two areas.

Wetmore, A. 1931c. The Pleistocene avifauna of Florida. Proc. Int. Ornithol. Congr. 7:479-483.
Condor bones.

Wetmore, A. 1932. Additional records of birds from cavern deposits in New Mexico. Condor 34(3):141-142.
Additional condor bones found.

Wetmore, A. 1933. The eagle, king of birds, and his kin. Natl. Geogr. Mag. 64(1):43-95.
General comments on the condor.

Wetmore, A. 1956. A check-list of the fossil and prehistoric birds of North America and the West Indies. Smithson. Misc. Coll. 131(5):1-105.
Listing of fossil locations.

Wetmore, A. 1959. Birds of the Pleistocene in North America. Smithson. Misc. Coll. 138(4):1-24.
General comments on prehistoric distribution.

Wetmore, A., and H. Friedmann. 1933. The California condor in Texas. Condor 35(1):37-38.
At least three condors represented in cave deposits, including one fledgling.

Whitaker, G. B. 1918. Capturing the great American condor. Overland Monthly 71(5):390-392.
Exciting account of taking condor egg and nestlings.

White, L. T., Jr. 1940. Changes in the popular concept of "California." Calif. Hist. Soc. Q. 19(3):219-224.
Suggests the name "California" may have been derived from Persian Kar-i-farn where the griffon vultures lived, because the namers saw condors (griffons).

Wilbur, M. E., ed. 1941. A pioneer at Sutter's Fort, 1846-1850. The adventures of Heinrich Lienhard. The Calafia Society, Los Angeles. 291 pp.
Condors seen along Sacramento River.

Wilbur, S. R. 1971. The condor's place. West. Tanager 37(11):1-2.
Philosophy of condor preservation.

Wilbur, S. R. 1972. The food resources of the California condor. U.S. Fish and Wildlife Service, Patuxent Wildlife Research Center. 18 pp.
Food as related to distribution and production.

Wilbur, S. R. 1973. The California condor in the Pacific Northwest. Auk 90(1):196-198.
Distribution, numbers, and evaluation of disappearance.

Wilbur, S. R. 1974a. California condor specimens in collections. Wilson Bull. 86(1):71-72.
One hundred eighty-five skins, 51 skeletons, 55 eggs.

Wilbur, S. R. 1974b. Future of the condor: recovery or extinction? Field Mus. Nat. Hist. Bull. 45(9):3-6.
Current status.

Wilbur, S. R. 1975a. California condor plumage and molt as field study aids. Calif. Fish Game 61(3):144-148.
Plumage characteristics of limited value in aging condors or separating individuals in the field.

Wilbur, S. R. 1975b. Recovery planning for the California condor. Outdoor Calif. 36(4):10-11.
Description of "recovery planning" process, including a statement of objectives of the California Condor Recovery Plan.

Wilbur, S. R. 1976a. Condor: a doomed species? Natl. Parks Conserv. Mag. 50(2):17-19.
Popular update of condor status and preservation efforts.

Wilbur, S. R. 1976b. Status of the California condor, 1972-1975. Am. Birds 30(4):789-790.
Distribution similar to previous years, production averaging less than 2 per year, and numbers declining to less than 50 total.

Wilbur, S. R. 1976c. Are there condors in our future? Audubon Imprint (Santa Monica Bay Audubon Society) 1(2):1-2, 5.
Captive propagation of condors discussed.

Wilbur, S. R., and J. C. Borneman. 1972. Copulation by California condors. Auk 89(2):444-445.
Copulation described.

Wilbur, S. R., W. D. Carrier, J. C. Borneman, and R. D. Mallette. 1972. Distribution and numbers of the California condor, 1966-1971. Am. Birds 26(5):819-823.
Summary of status to 1971.

Wilbur, S. R., W. D. Carrier, and J. C. Borneman. 1974. Supplemental feeding program for California condors. J. Wildl. Manage. 38(2):343-346.
Results of supplemental feeding: condors fed regularly, as did other scavengers.

Wilcox, A. 1901. California vulture. Am. Ornithol. 1(9):164-168.
General comments, collection records.

Wilcox, A. 1903. The California vulture. West. Field 2(4):217-219.
General comments, collection records.

Willett, G. 1908. Summer birds of the upper Salinas Valley and adjacent foothills. Condor 10(4):137-139.
Seen 14 years ago, but not recently.

Willett, G. 1912. Birds of the Pacific slope of southern California. Pac. Coast Avifauna 7:1-122.
Summary of egg collection data; condor considered "tolerably common."

Willett, G. 1931. The condor in San Benito County, California. Condor 33(1):31.
Egg collected, 6 April 1898; condors common in early 1880's, gone by 1900.

Willett, G. 1933. Revised list of birds of southwestern California. Pac. Coast Avifauna 21. 204 pp.
"No doubt that the condor has decreased in numbers during the last fifteen or twenty years."

Williams, Mrs. Will. 1950. [Letter regarding condors in Kern County, California.] News from the Bird-banders 25(4):50.
April 1950, 2 condors seen near Granite Station; hearsay report of 42 condors in area during ground squirrel poisoning in April 1949.

Wilson, A. V. 1928. Condor caught in San Joaquin Valley. Condor 30(5):159-160.
Kern County, 1926, condor chased by car, caught, let go.

Wolfe, B. 1971. The California condor: Conservancy helps protect bird facing extinction. Nat. Conserv. News 21(4):6-7.
Land acquisition near condor nest.

Wolfe, L. R. 1938. Eggs of the Falconiformes. Oologist's Rec. 18(1):2-10.
One condor egg laid in captivity.

Woods, R. S. 1929. Field identification of vultures. Auk 36(3):386.
Condor identification by color and flight pattern.

Wyman, L. E. 1924. A California condor in captivity. Condor 26(4):153.
At Selig Zoo, Los Angeles.

Young, B., and J. Young. 1965. Sovereign of California skies. Desert 28(4):8-9.
Popular account of life history and status.

Zimmerman, D. R. 1975. To save a bird in peril. Coward, McCann and Geoghegan, Inc., New York. 286 pp.
Pages 174-180, description of supplemental feeding programs for California condors and other raptors.